THE SCIENTIST VS. THE HUMANIST

Also in this series, under the general editorship of Erwin R. Steinberg

PERSONAL INTEGRITY
  Edited by William M. Schutte *and* Erwin R. Steinberg

THE RULE OF FORCE
  Edited by Erwin R. Steinberg

THE SCIENTIST
VS.
THE HUMANIST

Edited by *George Levine and Owen Thomas*

INDIANA UNIVERSITY

W · W · NORTON & COMPANY · INC   *New York*

CONTENTS

PREFACE

Among the classic debates of history, none has more relevance to our age than that between the scientist and the humanist. No debate is more central to society's definition of an educated man; no debate is more important to the student faced with the choice of a career. And no debate more clearly focuses the long-standing antagonism between those who see the meaning of life in terms of material progress and increased knowledge of the natural world and those who see it only in the personal fulfilment of every man's "humanity"—of his moral, intellectual, and aesthetic capacities. Perhaps the antagonism is artificial, perhaps not. There are no single or simple answers to the questions raised by the debate, although there are certainly wrong ones. For this reason, and because the problem extends beyond the general and social to the personal—to the very border of the whole modern problem of "personal identity"—each of us has an obligation to investigate the classic and the crude formulation of the problems and then to determine our own answers. The selections in this book provide a balanced beginning for such an investigation.

Although the debate can be traced back to classic times, the book includes no selections from times prior to the seventeenth and eighteenth centuries. It was at about this time, at the birth of modern science, that the problem took its modern shape. And since the debate affects not only our ideas but our experience of the world, there are selections from writers of fiction. Finally, since the debate cuts across society, there are selections from popular magazines and from scholarly journals. Taken together these selections bring the critical questions into focus. What is science? What kinds of values are inherent in the humanities? How can the advances of science and the heritage of the humanities be combined to the benefit of the individual and of society?

As there is no necessary order to these questions, so there was no necessary arrangement of selections within the book. Yet the arrangement is not arbitrary. The first selection is the shortened form of the notorious modern statement by C. P. Snow, who has been at the center of the controversy for at least a decade. This is followed by a careful definition of science by a humanist scientifically inclined, and this, in turn, by three pieces from past centuries which raise many of the modern problems. At the heart of the book are set—in essays by Matthew Arnold and T. H. Huxley—the classic nineteenth-century formulations of the problem as it relates to education. These are followed by Lionel Trilling's examination both of the nineteenth-century debate and of the contemporary, acrimonious debate between F. R. Leavis and Snow. Next, there are biographical sketches of a scientist, Charles Darwin, and of a humanist, William Butler Yeats, two men whose very lives suggest the nature of the conflict. There follow, after Whitman's famous poem dramatizing the romantic reaction to science, several recent works—one an extremely intelligent and amusing science-fiction story—which suggest how various writers and scientists have attempted to work out the problems to their personal satisfaction. The essays by Robert Oppenheimer and Howard Mumford Jones indicate the difficulty of making intelligible to the layman the problems of their divergent disciplines. At the conclusion is a forceful and complex statement of the possibilities of reconciliation between the two modes of knowledge. The bibliography, though necessarily very incomplete, offers a relatively wide variety of material for further reading.

Our thanks go to Nancy Dillingham, Valerie Gottesman, and especially Kay Dinsmoor who provided outstanding secretarial help, some of it beyond the call of duty; to Michael Wolff, who suggested some provocative questions; and, of course, to our wives, who contributed the understanding and encouragement necessary to the completion of the manuscript.

G. L.
O. T.

Bloomington, Indiana
February 20, 1963

THE TWO CULTURES

C. P. Snow

"It's rather odd," said G. H. Hardy, one afternoon in the early Thirties, "but when we hear about 'intellectuals' nowadays, it doesn't include people like me and J. J. Thomson and Rutherford." Hardy was the first mathematician of his generation, J. J. Thomson the first physicist of his; as for Rutherford, he was one of the greatest scientists who have ever lived. Some bright young literary person (I forget the exact context) putting them outside the enclosure reserved for intellectuals seemed to Hardy the best joke for some time. It does not seem quite such a good joke now. The separation between the two cultures has been getting deeper under our eyes; there is now precious little communication between them, little but different kinds of incomprehension and dislike.

The traditional culture, which is, of course, mainly literary, is behaving like a state whose power is rapidly declining—standing on its precarious dignity, spending far too much energy on Alexandrian intricacies, occasionally letting fly in fits of aggressive pique quite beyond its means, too much on the defensive to show any generous imagination to the forces which must inevitably reshape it. Whereas the scientific culture is expansive, not restrictive, confident at the roots, the more confident after its bout of Oppenheimerian self-criticism, certain that history is on its side, impatient, intolerant, creative rather than critical, good-natured and brash. Neither culture knows the virtues of the other; often it seems they deliberately do not want to know. The resentment which the traditional culture feels for the scientific is shaded with fear; from the

From the *New Statesman*, LII (October 6, 1956), 413–414. Reprinted by permission of C. P. Snow and the *New Statesman*.

other side, the resentment is not shaded so much as brimming with irritation. When scientists are faced with an expression of the traditional culture, it tends (to borrow Mr. William Cooper's eloquent phrase) to make their feet ache.

It does not need saying that generalisations of this kind are bound to look silly at the edges. There are a good many scientists indistinguishable from literary persons, and vice versa. Even the stereotype generalisations about scientists are misleading without some sort of detail—e.g., the generalisation that scientists as a group stand on the political Left. This is only partly true. A very high proportion of engineers is almost as conservative as doctors; of pure scientists, the same would apply to chemists. It is only among physicists and biologists that one finds the Left in strength. If one compared the whole body of scientists with their opposite numbers of the traditional culture (writers, academics, and so on), the total result might be a few per cent. more towards the Left wing, but not more than that. Nevertheless, as a first approximation, the scientific culture is real enough, and so is its difference from the traditional. For anyone like myself, by education a scientist, by calling a writer, at one time moving between groups of scientists and writers in the same evening, the difference has seemed dramatic.

The first thing, impossible to miss, is that scientists are on the up and up; they have the strength of a social force behind them. If they are English, they share the experience common to us all—of being in a country sliding economically downhill —but in addition (and to many of them it seems psychologically more important) they belong to something more than a profession, to something more like a directing class of a new society. In a sense oddly divorced from politics, they are the new men. Even the staidest and most politically conservative of scientific veterans, lurking in dignity in their colleges, have some kind of link with the world to come. They do not hate it as their colleagues do; part of their mind is open to it; almost against their will, there is a residual glimmer of kinship there. The young English scientists may and do curse their luck; increasingly they fret about the rigidities of their universities, about the ossification of the traditional culture which, to the scientists, makes the universities cold and dead; they violently envy their Russian counterparts who have money and equipment without discernible limit, who have the whole field wide open. But still they stay pretty resilient: they are swept on by the same social force. Harwell and Winscale have just as much spirit as Los Alamos and Chalk River: the neat petty bourgeois houses, the tough and clever young, the crowds of children: they are symbols, frontier towns.

There is a touch of the frontier qualities, in fact, about the whole scientific culture. Its tone is, for example, steadily heterosexual. The difference in social manners between Harwell and Hampstead, or as far as that goes between Los Alamos and Greenwich Village, would make an anthropologist blink. About the whole scientific culture, there is an absence —surprising to outsiders—of the feline and oblique. Sometimes it seems that scientists relish speaking the truth, especially when it is unpleasant. The climate of personal relations is singularly bracing, not to say harsh: it strikes bleakly on those unused to it, who suddenly find that the scientists' way of deciding on action is by a full-dress argument, with no regard for sensibilities and no holds barred. No body of people ever believed more in dialectic as the primary method of attaining sense; and if you want a picture of scientists in their off-moments it could be just one of a knock-about argument. Under the argument there glitter egotisms as rapacious as any of ours: but, unlike ours, the egotisms are driven by a common purpose.

How much of the traditional culture gets through to them? The answer is not simple. A good many scientists, including some of the most gifted, have the tastes of literary persons, read the same things, and read as much. Broadly, though, the infiltration is much less. History gets across to a certain extent, in particular social history: the sheer mechanics of living, how men ate, built, travelled, worked, touches a good many scientific imaginations, so they have fastened on such works as Trevelyan's *Social History*, and Professor Gordon Childe's books. Philosophy, the scientific culture views with indifference, especially metaphysics. As Rutherford said cheerfully to Samuel Alexander: "When you think of all the years you've been talk-

ing about those things, Alexander, and what does it all add
up to? *Hot air*, nothing but *hot air*." A bit less exuberantly,
that is what contemporary scientists would say. They regard
it as a major intellectual virtue, to know what not to think
about. They might touch their hats to linguistic analysis, as
a relatively honourable way of wasting time; not so to existentialism.

The arts? The only one which is cultivated among scientists
is music. It goes both wide and deep; there may possibly be
a greater density of musical appreciation than in the traditional culture. In comparison, the graphic arts (except architecture) score little, and poetry not at all. Some novels
work their way through, but not as a rule the novels which
literary persons set most value on. The two cultures have so
few points of contact that the diffusion of novels shows the
same sort of delay, and exhibits the same oddities, as though
they were getting into translation in a foreign country. It is
only fairly recently, for instance, that Graham Greene and
Evelyn Waugh have become more than names. And, just as
it is rather startling to find that in Italy Bruce Marshall is
by a long shot the best-known British novelist, so it jolts one
to hear scientists talking with attention of the works of Nevil
Shute. In fact, there is a good reason for that: Mr. Shute was
himself a high-class engineer, and a book like *No Highway*
is packed with technical stuff that is not only accurate but
often original. Incidentally, there are benefits to be gained from
listening to intelligent men, utterly removed from the literary
scene and unconcerned as to who's in and who's out. One can
pick up such a comment as a scientist once made, that it looked
to him as though the current preoccupations of the New
Criticism, the extreme concentration on a tiny passage, had
made us curiously insensitive to the total flavour of a work,
to its cumulative effects, to the epic qualities in literature. But,
on the other side of the coin, one is just as likely to listen to
three of the most massive intellects in Europe happily discussing the merits of *The Wallet of Kai-Lung*.

When you meet the younger rank-and-file of scientists, it
often seems that they do not read at all. The prestige of the
traditional culture is high enough for some of them to make

a gallant shot at it. Oddly enough, the novelist whose name to them has become a token of esoteric literary excellence is that difficult highbrow Dickens. They approach him in a grim and dutiful spirit as though tackling *Finnegan's Wake*, and feel a sense of achievement if they manage to read a book through. But most young technicians do not fly so high. When you ask them what they read—"As a married man," one says, "I prefer the garden." Another says: "I always like just to use my books as tools." (Difficult to resist speculating what kind of tool a book would make. A sort of hammer? A crude digging instrument?)

That, or something like it, is a measure of the incom-municability of the two cultures. On their side the scientists are losing a great deal. Some of that loss is inevitable: it must and would happen in any society at our technical level. But in this country we make it quite unnecessarily worse by our educational patterns. On the other side, how much does the traditional culture lose by the separation?

I am inclined to think, even more. Not only practically— we are familiar with those arguments by now—but also intellectually and morally. The intellectual loss is a little difficult to appraise. Most scientists would claim that you cannot comprehend the world unless you know the structure of science, in particular of physical science. In a sense, and a perfectly genuine sense, that is true. Not to have read *War and Peace* and *La Cousine Bette* and *La Chartreuse de Parme* is not to be educated; but so is not to have a glimmer of the Second Law of Thermodynamics. Yet that case ought not to be pressed too far. It is more justifiable to say that those with-out any scientific understanding miss a whole body of ex-perience: they are rather like the tone deaf, from whom all musical experience is cut off and who have to get on without it. The intellectual invasions of science are, however, penetrat-ing deeper. Psycho-analysis once looked like a deep invasion, but that was a false alarm; cybernetics may turn out to be the real thing, driving down into the problems of will and cause and motive. If so, those who do not understand the method will not understand the depths of their own cultures.

But the greatest enrichment the scientific culture could give us is—though it does not originate like that—a moral one. Among scientists, deep-natured men know, as starkly as any men have known, that the individual human condition is tragic; for all its triumphs and joys, the essence of it is loneliness and the end death. But what they will not admit is that, because the individual condition is tragic, therefore the social condition must be tragic, too. Because a man must die, that is no excuse for his dying before his time and after a servile life. The impulse behind the scientists drives them to limit the area of tragedy, to take nothing as tragic that can conceivably lie within men's will. They have nothing but contempt for those representatives of the traditional culture who use a deep insight into man's fate to obscure the social truth—or to do something pettier than obscure the truth, just to hang on to a few perks. Dostoevski sucking up to the Chancellor Pobe-donostsev, who thought the only thing wrong with slavery was that there was not enough of it; the political decadence of the *avant garde* of 1914, with Ezra Pound finishing up broadcasting for the Fascists; Claudel agreeing sanctimoniously with the Marshal about the virtue in others' suffering; Faulkner giving sentimental reasons for treating Negroes as a different species. They are all symptoms of the deepest temptation of the clerks—which is to say: "Because man's condition is tragic, everyone ought to stay in their place, with mine as it happens somewhere near the top." From that particular temptation, made up of defeat, self-indulgence, and moral vanity, the scientific culture is almost totally immune. It is that kind of moral health of the scientists which, in the last few years, the rest of us have needed most; and of which, because the two cultures scarcely touch, we have been most deprived.

WHAT SCIENCE IS

H. J. Muller

Roughly stated, the scientific method is to go and look, and then look again. The most elaborate experiments and abstruse equations are designed to answer the simple question, "What are the facts?" Today this question seems so natural and obviously sensible that it is hard to understand how for centuries men could repeat Pliny's statement, that the blood of a goat would shatter a diamond, when a simple test would have disproved it. Yet it seems that they did not perform the test; and the explanation is that the basis of their thought was not empirical but "rational." Although Aristotle went to nature, he returned for authority to pure reason. He simply asserted that heavy bodies must fall faster than light ones, just as he asserted that planets move in circles because the circle is the only perfect figure. Hence Galileo's Pisa experiment marked a real revolution in thought. It marked, Dewey summarizes:

a change from the qualitative to the quantitative or metric; from the heterogeneous to the homogeneous; from intrinsic form to relations; from esthetic harmonies to mathematical formulae; from contemplative enjoyment to active manipulation and control; from rest to change; from eternal objects to temporal sequence.

In this summary, science already begins to look strange to the plain man; and of course it is strange. Even as roughly stated, its method is still not generally applied to moral, political, or other problems. For science is not, strictly, "organized common sense." Common sense is not only much vaguer and more cocksure but in a way, curiously, more practical. It deals with the total concrete situation, takes life as it comes. Science always abstracts for a very limited purpose, makes up fictions. Especially in late years, it has left common

From H. J. Muller, *Science and Criticism*, Chap. III. Reprinted by permission of the Yale University Press.

sense far behind. When scientists try to speak the plain man's language, they tell him that the quantum theory may be understood by the analogy of a clock whose mechanism had vanished, leaving only the ticks, and that if he still doesn't understand, the point is that the universe is "not only queerer than we suppose, but queerer that we *can* suppose."

Yet science does remain simply a form of organized intelligence; to become oriented to it, we again do well to begin with the obvious. Although men talk as if the object of intelligence were the discovery and contemplation of eternal truths, actually they employ it chiefly to handle the new situations that are always arising even in a routine life. In daily experience they are continually experimenting, reconstructing, adjusting themselves to a continually changing environment; otherwise there could be no consciousness, no real experience at all. The scientific method is a systematic extension of this behaviour. George H. Mead therefore described it as "only the evolutionary process grown self-conscious." Biologically, it is an advance in the natural direction: more differentiation, finer adaptation to environment, greater control over environment.

Similarly the basic interests of science, the concern with the "material" world, are not actually newfangled or alien. Men often feel that nature is hostile to them, at best very careless, at worst unfathomably cruel; in their philosophies they have represented it as a show of illusory or accidental appearances, in their religions as a mess of devil's pottage. Nevertheless they also feel a deep and constant kinship. They naturally personify the world about them and draw from it their metaphors for human life: they bud and bloom in youth, they ripen like fruit on the bough, they fall into the sere, the yellow leaf. The rhythms of nature are in their blood. Like poetry, science explores and articulates these relations; it realizes our rich heritage as children of this earth. Like Christian theology, moreover, it assumes that the heritage is lawful. Science grew out of the medieval faith that the world is orderly and rational, and that all happenings in it could be explained. Scientists now consider this a postulate, not a fact, and their explanations are usually offensive to orthodox theologians; nevertheless they have the same working faith as the theologians. Thus Newton could lay the foundations of the mechanistic universe in a spirit of extreme piety, and be applauded by other devout Christians; he was simply clarifying the ways of God to man. Thus agnostic scientists still admire all the evidence of uniformity, regularity, harmony in the universe. They admire the most wonderful of miracles, that there are not incessant miracles.

In other words, they are not really so inhuman as they are reputed to be. Whereas the man on the street sees only the gadgetry of science, intellectuals are prone to the other extreme of viewing it always in the abstract. They dwell upon its remorseless impersonality, the coldness of its truth; they forget its personal satisfactions, the imaginative value of its truths. For to scientists truth is indeed beauty. Mathematicians exclaim over the "elegance" of their demonstrations, Einstein delights in the "pre-established harmonies" that physicists discover, J. W. N. Sullivan is struck by the "astonishing beauty and symmetry" that Minkowski gave the theory of relativity by adding the notion of a four-dimensional continuum. On the other hand, they are displeased by unsightly gaps or bulges in their theory-patterns, dislike the messiness of quantum physics even when its theories seem to fit the facts. Their effort is always to get all their facts to fall into a shape, and their preference among theories, when the experimental test has yet to decide, appears to be determined chiefly by the esthetic quality of the shape. Thus Sullivan notes the comments of Einstein and Eddington on each other's attempt to reduce the laws of electromagnetism to geometry: Einstein said he simply did not "like" Eddington's theory, though he could not disprove it, and Eddington said Einstein's theory was a matter of "taste." Altogether, the generic motive of science is no doubt utilitarian—"service to mankind," if one likes more exalted terms; but the individual scientist, like the individual artist, does his work for the simple, unexalted reason that he likes it, and when it turns out right he feels a comparable lift and glow.

This demonstration that even the scientist is human may seem inconsequential. It finally leads, however, to the heart of the problem of what science is. The recent developments in

its philosophy may be summed up in precisely this recognition
of the "human element," the human "standpoint" that is
literally involved in all statements. Scientific laws are not chips
off the old block Reality; as interpretations of sense impressions,
they take after the human mind as well. All knowledge is a
joint enterprise, an affair whose conditions are both inside and
outside the organism. It is the offspring of the marriage of
man and nature, a union in which the older partner may be
expected to outlive the younger but which is indissoluble during
the life of man.

This idea will concern us later on. Immediately, Einstein
tells us how to understand the scientist's method: "Don't listen
to his words, examine his achievements." Still better, watch
him at work, examine the actual operations by which he gets
his knowledge; and here an excellent guide is William H.
George's *The Scientist in Action*. Whatever is may become
in theory, George points out, a scientific fact is in practice an
observation of coincidences. Although products of sensory impression, facts are impersonal in that they are independent of
the judgment of any one man; they are statements of coincidences that can be observed under the same conditions by all
men. The scientist can therefore gather and test them without
bothering about such philosophical problems as whether there
really is an external world; "real" is not an observable property.
He does have to bother, however, with the problem of classify-
ing and interpreting his facts, fitting them into patterns called
theories and laws. The more comprehensive these are, the
better he is pleased; but the most comprehensive is still
tentative and does not "reduce by one the number of absolute
truths to be discovered." Newton's great laws were patterns into
which hitherto unconnected facts could be fitted; Einstein
devised a different pattern that could accommodate all these
and other facts; and we may expect that more inclusive but
still different patterns will be devised by Zweinstein, Dreistein,
etc.

In other words, facts and figures do *not* speak for themselves.
For all their stubbornness, they are accommodating enough
to allow a number of different interpretations—and there are
always enough of them around to support almost any theory.

Moreover, the facts are not simply there, waiting in line to be discovered. The scientist selects from a host of possibilities, he looks *for* as well as *at*, he may accordingly *overlook*—as Grimaldi's experiments on the path of light were long neglected because they did not fit in with Newton's corpuscular theory. Hence the advance of science has not been automatic or really systematic, and it has not been in a straight line. Science is first of all the creation of scientists, who are also men with temperaments, special interests, predispositions. (Bertrand Russell has noted, for example, the divergent developments in animal psychology under Thorndike and Koehler: "Animals studied by Americans rush about frantically, with an incredible display of hustle and pep, and at last achieve the desired result by chance. Animals observed by Germans sit still and think, and at last evolve the solution out of their inner consciousness.") More significantly, science is the creation of a definite type of mentality, which has been interested in certain kinds of phenomena but notoriously indifferent to others, averse to the seeming "wild data." Most significantly, it is the creation of a culture, a society with special interests. Even physics, which seems wholly impersonal and autonomous, has been influenced by vested social interests. The concept of energy was developed to meet the manufacturers' need of a bookkeeping device, a way of measuring the efficiency of machines in units of work; in general there is an obvious correspondence between the long reign of classical mechanics and the needs of industry. Today, when science has developed a highly specialized technique, language, and subject matter of its own, it is still dependent upon the greater society for its privileges. It is the more profoundly a fashion of the times.

This view is not designed to humble or discredit the scientist. Rather it relieves him of the awful responsibility of speaking absolute truth. It stresses his continuity with the organic processes of evolution, the tremendous adventure of civilization, the vital needs and purposes of society; the scientist no more than the poet can afford the illusion that his activity is pure or priestly. It makes clearer the cultural pattern of science today: the concept itself of patterns, fields, organic wholes, which has become important in all the sciences, and which parallels the collectivistic trend in the world of affairs. And it enables a more realistic approach, specifically, to the difficult issue of just where science properly begins and ends.

The popular notion is that science necessarily involves the use of instruments in a laboratory. Knowledge cannot be really scientific unless men have got it out of a test tube, taken an X-ray picture of it, or tried it out on some guinea pigs. Such methods are very well for dealings with sticks and stones, animal life, or the human body; but it follows that they cannot apply to the motions of mind or spirit. Laboratory workers themselves are often contemptuous of the social sciences, and of psychology when it leaves the laboratory and deals with such immeasurables as "consciousness" and "insight." They distrust any statement that cannot be put into an equation. And so the critic is warned off the sciences of man, which are naturally closest to his interests. He is left with the problem of determining just where, then, the sciences stop and the humanities begin, and just what use he can make of the power that has in any event so thoroughly made over the world in which the humanities have their being.

To begin with, there are important distinctions that should remain distinct. Some generous philosophers identify science with all disciplined thought, uniting all the humanities and the sciences in one big happy family. Thus Cassius J. Keyser defines science as any work that aims to establish by legitimate means a body of categorical propositions about the actual world; he therefore accepts as science the work of Plato and Aristotle—and blurs the fundamental difference between their thought and the thought of Galileo or Darwin. Moreover, there are important differences between the sciences. The physicist and the chemist have the adventitious advantage of large subsidies (capitalism has been a generous if not a disinterested patron) and now of relative freedom from personal prejudice or official interference; the psychologist and the sociologist are at any moment likely to tread on the corns of public opinion or get mixed up in some live social issue. But the former also have the intrinsic advantage of a subject matter that lends itself to the extremely helpful devices of mathematical measurement and controlled experiment. The

experimental test is especially important, as the ultimate criterion for distinguishing scientific knowledge from philosophic
speculation.

Nevertheless most distinguished scientists appear to agree
with Max Planck, that from physics to sociology there is a
continuous chain; and I can see no practical or logical reason
for choosing to break the chain. On practical grounds, it would
seem desirable to give science as much scope as possible, and
not to discourage important social inquiries by verbal quibbles
or qualms about their scientific chastity; it would seem foolish
to demand complete positive knowledge or none. On logical
grounds, any sharp break in the chain is not only arbitrary but
inconsistent with the basic scientific assumption of natural
continuity. That the physical sciences are more objective and
more exact than the sciences of man makes them neither more
fundamental nor fundamentally different. The differences are
in degree, not in kind.

Ultimately the unity of science lies in the logic not the
materials or the specific techniques of its inquiry. As formulated
by Dewey in his monumental work, this is a logic of discovery
and invention. Its forms are not a priori but postulational and
operational; they are not absolute modes of pure reason but
generalizations drawn from previous inquiry and liable to
modification by subsequent discoveries. Indeed, scientists object to any theory, such as vitalism in biology, which is complete and therefore offers no possibility of advance; their curious
objection, J. H. Woodger observes, is that it is *too* successful,
too perfect. They demand that all theories live dangerously.
But this experimental logic does not absolutely require the
specific technique of laboratory experiment. It requires primarily that theories be so formulated as to leave room for
future discoveries and almost certain modifications. It thereby
exposes, indeed, the essential weakness of the sciences of man
today, which is not so much the jungle growth of theory as
the attitude toward this theory. As scientists, psychologists
and sociologists are still very young, and like youngsters much
too cocky—few physicists speak with quite the assurance of
John B. Watson or Pareto. More specifically, they are seldom
content with mere postulates and approximates; they set up

some explanatory principle as necessary and sufficient, the one positive truth by which all the other little truths must be sired or certified. Yet their attitude is quite gratuitous. This very criticism of it implies that an experimental logic can be applied to these problems too.

"Wherever there is the slightest possibility of the human mind to *know*," wrote Karl Pearson, "there is a legitimate problem of science." If men have "known" all sorts of absurdities, there can be no question about a fact, strictly defined, and such facts are available in all spheres of interest. Observation, not measurement of coincidences, is their criterion. If it is clearly more difficult to classify and interpret them in the sciences of man, it is not clearly impossible; important relations have already been established and systematically formulated. Students of the humanities who deny that there are fundamental laws in their province necessarily think in a way that presupposes such laws—else their thought would be pointless. In sum, only by divorcing human affairs from natural processes can they be shut off from scientific inquiry; and this ancient expedient disposes of the problem by creating two more.

GULLIVER'S TRAVELS:
A Voyage to Laputa

Jonathan Swift

THE AUTHOR PERMITTED TO SEE THE GRAND ACADEMY OF LAGADO. THE ACADEMY LARGELY DESCRIBED. THE ARTS WHEREIN THE PROFESSORS EMPLOY THEMSELVES.

This Academy is not an entire single building, but a continuation of several houses on both sides of a street, which growing waste was purchased and applied to that use.

I was received very kindly by the Warden, and went for many days to the Academy. Every room hath in it one or more projectors, and I believe I could not be in fewer than five hundred rooms.

The first man I saw was of a meagre aspect, with sooty hands and face, his hair and beard long, ragged and singed in several places. His clothes, shirt, and skin were all of the same colour. He had been eight years upon a project for extracting sun-beams out of cucumbers, which were to be put into vials hermetically sealed, and let out to warm the air in raw inclement summers. He told me he did not doubt in eight years more he should be able to supply the Governor's gardens with sunshine at a reasonable rate; but he complained that his stock was low, and entreated me to give him something as an encouragement to ingenuity, especially since this had been a very dear season for cucumbers. I made him a small present, for my lord had furnished me with money on purpose, because he knew their practice of begging from all who go to see them.

I went into another chamber, but was ready to hasten back, being almost overcome with a horrible stink. My conductor pressed me forward, conjuring me in a whisper to give no offence, which would be highly resented, and therefore I durst not so much as stop my nose. The projector of this cell was the most ancient student of the Academy; his face and beard were of a pale yellow; his hands and clothes daubed over with filth. When I was presented to him, he gave me a close embrace (a compliment I could well have excused). His employment from his first coming into the Academy, was an operation to reduce human excrement to its original food, by separating the several parts, removing the tincture which it receives from the gall, making the odour exhale, and scumming off the saliva. He had a weekly allowance from the society, of a vessel filled with human ordure, about the bigness of a Bristol barrel.

I saw another at work to calcine ice into gunpowder, who likewise showed me a treatise he had written concerning the malleability of fire, which he intended to publish.

There was a most ingenious architect who had contrived a new method for building houses, by beginning at the roof, and working downwards to the foundation, which he justified to me by the like practice of those two prudent insects, the bee and the spider.

There was a man born blind, who had several apprentices in his own condition: their employment was to mix colours for painters, which their master taught them to distinguish by feeling and smelling. It was indeed my misfortune to find them at that time not very perfect in their lessons, and the professor himself happened to be generally mistaken: this artist is much encouraged and esteemed by the whole fraternity.

In another apartment I was highly pleased with a projector, who had found a device of ploughing the ground with hogs, to save the charges of ploughs, cattle, and labour. The method is this: in an acre of ground you bury, at six inches distance and eight deep, a quantity of acorns, dates, chestnuts, and other mast or vegetables whereof these animals are fondest; then you drive six hundred or more of them into the field, where in a few days they will root up the whole ground in search of their food, and make it fit for sowing, at the same time manuring it with their dung. It is true, upon experiment they found the charge and trouble very great, and they had little or no crop. However, it is not doubted that this invention may be capable of great improvement.

I went into another room, where the walls and ceiling were all hung round with cobwebs, except a narrow passage for the artist to go in and out. At my entrance he called aloud to me not to disturb his webs. He lamented the fatal mistake the world had been so long in of using silk-worms, while we had such plenty of domestic insects, who infinitely excelled the former, because they understood how to weave as well as spin. And he proposed farther that by employing spiders the charge of dyeing silks should be wholly saved, whereof I was fully convinced when he showed me a vast number of flies most beautifully coloured, wherewith he fed his spiders, assuring us that the webs would take a tincture from them; and as he had them of all hues, he hoped to fit everybody's fancy, as soon as he could find proper food for the flies, of certain gums, oils, and other glutinous matter to give a strength and consistence to the threads.

There was an astronomer who had undertaken to place a sundial upon the great weathercock on the town-house, by adjusting the annual and diurnal motions of the earth and sun, so as to answer and coincide with all accidental turnings by the wind.

I was complaining of a small fit of the colic, upon which my conductor led me into a room, where a great physician resided, who was famous for curing that disease by contrary operations from the same instrument. He had a large pair of bellows with a long slender muzzle of ivory. This he conveyed eight inches up the anus, and drawing in the wind, he affirmed he could make the guts as lank as a dried bladder. But when the disease was more stubborn and violent, he let in the muzzle while the bellows were full of wind, which he discharged into the body of the patient, then withdrew the instrument to replenish it, clapping his thumb strongly against the orifice of the fundament; and this being repeated three or four times, the adventitious wind would rush out, bringing the noxious along with it (like water put into a pump), and the patient recover. I saw him try both experiments upon a dog, but could not discern any effect from the former. After the latter, the animal was ready to burst, and made so violent a discharge, as was very offensive to me and my companions. The dog died on the spot, and we left the doctor endeavouring to recover him by the same operation.

I visited many other apartments, but shall not trouble my reader with all the curiosities I observed, being studious of brevity.

I had hitherto seen only one side of the Academy, the other being appropriated to the advancers of speculative learning, of whom I shall say something when I have mentioned one illustrious person more, who is called among them *the universal artist*. He told us he had been thirty years employing his thoughts for the improvement of human life. He had two large rooms full of wonderful curiosities, and fifty men at work. Some were condensing air into a dry tangible substance, by extracting the nitre, and letting the aqueous or fluid particles percolate; others softening marble for pillows and pin-cushions; others petrifying the hoofs of a living horse to preserve them from foundering. The artist himself was at that time busy upon two great designs; the first, to sow land with chaff, wherein he

affirmed the true seminal virtue to be contained, as he demonstrated by several experiments which I was not skilful enough
to comprehend. The other was, by a certain composition of
gums, minerals, and vegetables outwardly applied, to prevent
the growth of wool upon two young lambs; and he hoped in a
reasonable time to propagate the breed of naked sheep all over
the kingdom.

We crossed a walk to the other part of the Academy, where,
as I have already said, the projectors in speculative learning
resided.

The first professor I saw was in a very large room, with forty
pupils about him. After salutation, observing me to look ear-
nestly upon a frame, which took up the greatest part of both
the length and breadth of the room, he said perhaps I might
wonder to see him employed in a project for improving speculative knowledge by practical and mechanical operations. But the
world would soon be sensible of its usefulness, and he flattered
himself that a more noble exalted thought never sprang in any
other man's head. Every one knew how laborious the usual
method is of attaining to arts and sciences; whereas by his contrivance the most ignorant person at a reasonable charge, and
with a little bodily labour, may write books in philosophy,
poetry, politics, law, mathematics, and theology, without the
least assistance from genius or study. He then led me to the
frame, about the sides whereof all his pupils stood in ranks. It
was twenty foot square, placed in the middle of the room. The
superficies was composed of several bits of wood, about the
bigness of a die, but some larger than others. They were all
linked together by slender wires. These bits of wood were covered on every square with paper pasted on them, and on these
papers were written all the words of their language, in their
several moods, tenses, and declensions, but without any order.
The professor then desired me to observe, for he was going to
set his engine at work. The pupils at his command took each of
them hold of an iron handle, whereof there were forty fixed
round the edges of the frame, and giving them a sudden turn,
the whole disposition of the words was entirely changed. He
then commanded six and thirty of the lads to read the several

lines softly as they appeared upon the frame; and where they found three or four words together that might make part of a sentence, they dictated to the four remaining boys who were scribes. This work was repeated three or four times, and at every turn the engine was so contrived that the words shifted into new places, as the square bits of wood moved upside down.

Six hours a day the young students were employed in this labour, and the professor showed me several volumes in large folio already collected, of broken sentences, which he intended to piece together, and out of those rich materials to give the world a complete body of all arts and sciences; which however might be still improved, and much expedited, if the public would raise a fund for making and employing five hundred such frames in Lagado, and oblige the managers to contribute in common their several collections.

He assured me, that this invention had employed all his thoughts from his youth, that he had emptied the whole vocabulary into his frame, and made the strictest computation of the general proposition there is in books between the numbers of particles, nouns, and verbs, and other parts of speech.

I made my humblest acknowledgement to this illustrious person for his great communicativeness, and promised if ever I had the good fortune to return to my native country, that I would do him justice, as the sole inventor of this wonderful machine; the form and contrivance of which I desired leave to delineate upon paper, as in the figure here annexed. I told him, although it were the custom of our learned in Europe to steal inventions from each other, who had thereby at least this advantage, that it became a controversy which was the right owner, yet I would take such caution, that he should have the honour entire without a rival.

We next went to the school of languages, where three professors sat in consultation upon improving that of their own country.

The first project was to shorten discourse by cutting polysyllables into one, and leaving out verbs and participles, because in reality all things imaginable are but nouns.

The other project was a scheme for entirely abolishing all

words whatsoever; and this was urged as a great advantage in point of health as well as brevity. For it is plain that every word we speak is in some degree a diminution of our lungs by corrosion, and consequently contributes to the shortening of our lives. An expedient was therefore offered, that since words are only names for *things*, it would be more convenient for all men to carry about them such things as were necessary to express the particular business they are to discourse on. And this invention would certainly have taken place, to the great ease as well as health of the subject, if the women, in conjunction with the vulgar and illiterate, had not threatened to raise a rebellion, unless they might be allowed the liberty to speak with their tongues, after the manner of their ancestors; such constant irreconcilable enemies to science are the common people. However, many of the most learned and wise adhere to the new scheme of expressing themselves by things, which hath only this inconvenience attending it, that if a man's business be very great, and of various kinds, he must be obliged in proportion to carry a great bundle of things upon his back, unless he can afford one or two strong servants to attend him. I have often beheld two of those sages almost sinking under the weight of their packs, like pedlars among us; who, when they met in the streets, would lay down their loads, open their sacks, and hold conversation for an hour together; then put up their implements, help each other to resume their burthens, and take their leave.

But for short conversations a man may carry implements in his pockets and under his arms, enough to supply him, and in his house he cannot be at a loss. Therefore the room where company meet who practise this art, is full of all things ready at hand, requisite to furnish matter for this kind of artificial converse.

Another great advantage proposed by this invention was that it would serve as an universal language to be understood in all civilised nations, whose goods and utensils are generally of the same kind, or nearly resembling, so that their uses might easily be comprehended. And thus ambassadors would be qualified to treat with foreign princes or ministers of state, to whose tongues they were utter strangers.

I was at the mathematical school, where the master taught his pupils after a method scarce imaginable to us in Europe. The proposition and demonstration were fairly written on a thin wafer, with ink composed of a cephalic tincture. This the student was to swallow upon a fasting stomach, and for three days following eat nothing but bread and water. As the wafer digested, the tincture mounted to his brain, bearing the proposition along with it. But the success hath not hitherto been answerable, partly by some error in the *quantum* or composition, and partly by the perverseness of lads, to whom this bolus is so nauseous, that they generally steal aside, and discharge it upwards before it can operate; neither have they been yet persuaded to use so long an abstinence as the prescription requires.

THE RAMBLER, NUMBER IX

Samuel Johnson

It is pleasing to contemplate a manufacture rising gradually from its first mean state by the successive labours of innumerable minds; to consider the first hollow trunk of an oak, in which, perhaps, the shepherd could scarce venture to cross a brook swelled with a shower, enlarged at last into a ship of war, attacking fortresses, terrifying nations, setting storms and billows at defiance, and visiting the remotest parts of the globe. And it might contribute to dispose us to a kinder regard for the labours of one another, if we were to consider from what unpromising beginnings the most useful productions of art have probably arisen. Who, when he saw the first sand or ashes, by a casual intenseness of heat melted into a metalline form, rugged with excrescences, and clouded with impurities, would have imagined, that in this formless lump lay concealed so many conveniencies of life, as would in time constitute a great part of the happiness of the world? Yet by some such fortuitous lique-

faction was mankind taught to procure a body at once in a high
degree solid and transparent, which might admit the light of
the sun, and exclude the violence of the wind; which might ex-
tend the sight of the philosopher to new ranges of existence,
and charm him at one time with the unbounded extent of the
material creation, and at another with the endless subordination
of animal life, and, what is yet of more importance, might supply the decays of nature, and succour old age with subsidiary
sight. Thus was the first artificer in glass employed, though
without his own knowledge or expectation. He was facilitating
and prolonging the enjoyment of light, enlarging the avenues of
science, and conferring the highest and most lasting pleasures;
he was enabling the student to contemplate nature, and the
beauty to behold herself.

HARD TIMES

Charles Dickens

CHAPTER I. THE ONE THING NEEDFUL

"Now, what I want is, Facts. Teach these boys and girls nothing but Facts. Facts alone are wanted in life. Plant nothing else,
and root out everything else. You can only form the minds of
reasoning animals upon Facts; nothing else will ever be of any
service to them. This is the principle on which I bring up my
own children, and this is the principle on which I bring up
these children. Stick to Facts, sir!"

The scene was a plain, bare, monotonous vault of a school-
room, and the speaker's square forefinger emphasized his observations by underscoring every sentence with a line on the
schoolmaster's sleeve. The emphasis was helped by the speaker's square wall of a forehead, which had his eyebrows for its
base, while his eyes found commodious cellarage in two dark
caves overshadowed by the wall. The emphasis was helped by
the speaker's mouth, which was wide, thin, and hard set. The

emphasis was helped by the speaker's voice, which was inflexible, dry, and dictatorial. The emphasis was helped by the speaker's hair, which bristled on the skirts of his bald head, a plantation of firs to keep the wind from its shining surface, all covered with knobs, like the crust of a plum pie, as if the head had scarcely warehouse room for the hard facts stored inside. The speaker's obstinate carriage, square coat, square legs, square shoulders,—nay, his very neckcloth, trained to take him by the throat with an unaccommodating grasp, like a stubborn fact, as it was, all helped the emphasis.

"In this life, we want nothing but Facts, sir; nothing but Facts!"

The speaker, and the schoolmaster, and the third grown person present, all backed a little, and swept with their eyes the inclined plane of little vessels then and there arranged in order, ready to have imperial gallons of facts poured into them until they were full to the brim.

CHAPTER II. MURDERING THE INNOCENTS

Thomas Gradgrind, sir. A man of realities. A man of facts and calculations. A man who proceeds upon the principle that two and two are four, and nothing over, and who is not to be talked into allowing for anything over. Thomas Gradgrind, sir —peremptorily Thomas—Thomas Gradgrind. With a rule and a pair of scales, and the multiplication table always in his pocket, sir, ready to weigh and measure any parcel of human nature, and tell you exactly what it comes to. It is a mere question of figures, a case of simple arithmetic. You might hope to get some other nonsensical belief into the head of George Gradgrind, or Augustus Gradgrind, or John Gradgrind, or Joseph Gradgrind (all suppositious, non-existent persons), but into the head of Thomas Gradgrind—no, sir!

In such terms Mr. Gradgrind always mentally introduced himself, whether to his private circle of acquaintance, or to the public in general. In such terms, no doubt, substituting the words "boys and girls" for "sir," Thomas Gradgrind now presented Thomas Gradgrind to the little pitchers before him, who were to be filled so full of facts.

Indeed, as he eagerly sparkled at them from the cellarage before mentioned, he seemed a kind of cannon loaded to the muzzle with facts, and prepared to blow them clean out of the regions of childhood at one discharge. He seemed a galvanizing apparatus, too, charged with a grim mechanical substitute for the tender young imaginations that were to be stormed away.

"Girl number twenty," said Mr. Gradgrind, squarely pointing with his square forefinger, "I don't know that girl. Who is that girl?"

"Sissy Jupe, sir," explained number twenty, blushing, standing up, and curtsying.

"Sissy is not a name," said Mr. Gradgrind. "Don't call yourself Sissy. Call yourself Cecilia."

"It's father as calls me Sissy, sir," returned the young girl in a trembling voice, and with another curtsy.

"Then he has no business to do it," said Mr. Gradgrind. "Tell him he mustn't. Cecilia Jupe. Let me see. What is your father?"

"He belongs to the horse-riding, if you please, sir."

Mr. Gradgrind frowned, and waved off the objectionable calling with his hand.

"We don't want to know anything about that, here. You mustn't tell us about that, here. Your father breaks horses, don't he?"

"If you please, sir, when they can get any to break, they do break horses in the ring, sir."

"You mustn't tell us about the ring, here. Very well, then. Describe your father as a horsebreaker. He doctors sick horses, I dare say?"

"Oh, yes, sir."

"Very well, then. He is a veterinary surgeon, a farrier, and horsebreaker. Give me your definition of a horse."

(Sissy Jupe thrown into the greatest alarm by this demand.)

"Girl number twenty unable to define a horse!" said Mr. Gradgrind, for the general behoof of the little pitchers. "Girl number twenty possessed of no facts, in reference to one of the commonest of animals! Some boy's definition of a horse.

Bitzer, yours."

The square finger, moving here and there, lighted suddenly on Bitzer, perhaps because he chanced to sit in the same ray of sunlight which, darting in at one of the bare windows of the intensely whitewashed room, irradiated Sissy. For the boys and girls sat on the face of the inclined plane in two compact bodies, divided up the centre by a narrow interval; and Sissy, being at the corner of a row on the sunny side, came in for the beginning of a sunbeam, of which Bitzer, being at the corner of a row on the other side, a few rows in advance, caught the end. But, whereas the girl was so dark-eyed and dark-haired that she seemed to receive a deeper and more lustrous colour from the sun when it shone upon her, the boy was so light-eyed and light-haired that the self-same rays appeared to draw out of him what little colour he ever possessed. His cold eyes would hardly have been eyes, but for the short ends of lashes which, by bringing them into immediate contrast with something paler than themselves, expressed their form. His short-cropped hair might have been a mere continuation of the sandy freckles on his forehead and face. His skin was so unwholesomely deficient in the natural tinge, that he looked as though, if he were cut, he would bleed white.

"Bitzer," said Thomas Gradgrind, "your definition of a horse."

"Quadruped. Graminivorous. Forty teeth, namely twenty-four grinders, four eye-teeth, and twelve incisive. Sheds coat in the spring; in marshy countries, sheds hoofs too. Hoofs hard, but requiring to be shod with iron. Age known by marks in mouth." Thus (and much more) Bitzer.

"Now girl number twenty," said Mr. Gradgrind, "you know what a horse is."

She curtsied again, and would have blushed deeper, if she could have blushed deeper than she had blushed all this time. Bitzer, after rapidly blinking at Thomas Gradgrind with both eyes at once, and so catching the light upon his quivering ends of lashes that they looked like the antennae of busy insects, put his knuckles to his freckled forehead, and sat down again.

The third gentleman now stepped forth. A mighty man at cutting and drying he was; a government officer; in his way

and in most other people's too), a professed pugilist; always
in training, always with a system to force down the general
throat like a bolus, always to be heard of at the bar of his
little Public-office, ready to fight All England. To continue
in fistic phraseology, he had a genius for coming up to the
scratch, wherever and whatever it was, and proving himself
an ugly customer. He would go in and damage any subject
whatever with his right, follow up with his left, stop, exchange,
counter, bore his opponent (he always fought All England)
to the ropes, and fall upon him neatly. He was certain to
knock the wind out of common-sense, and render that unlucky
adversary deaf to the call of time. And he had it in charge
from high authority to bring about the great public-office
Millennium, when Commissioners should reign upon earth.

"Very well," said this gentleman, briskly smiling, and fold-
ing his arms. "That's a horse. Now, let me ask you girls and
boys, would you paper a room with representations of horses?"

After a pause, one half of the children cried in chorus, "Yes,
sir!" Upon which the other half, seeing in the gentleman's face
that Yes was wrong, cried out in chorus, "No, sir!"—as the
custom is, in these examinations.

"Of course, no. Why wouldn't you?"

A pause. One corpulent slow boy, with a wheezy manner of
breathing, ventured the answer, Because he wouldn't paper a
room at all, but would paint it.

"You *must* paper it," said the gentleman, rather warmly.

"You must paper it," said Thomas Gradgrind, "whether you
like it or not. Don't tell *us* you wouldn't paper it. What do
you mean, boy?"

"I'll explain to you, then," said the gentleman, after another
and a dismal pause, "why you wouldn't paper a room with
representations of horses. Do you ever see horses walking up
and down the sides of rooms in reality—in fact? Do you?"

"Yes, sir!" from one half. "No, sir!" from the other.

"Of course, no," said the gentleman, with an indignant look
at the wrong half. "Why, then, you are not to see anywhere
what you don't see in fact; you are not to have anywhere what
you don't have in fact. What is called Taste is only another
name for Fact."

Thomas Gradgrind nodded his approbation.

"This is a new principle, a discovery, a great discovery," said the gentleman. "Now, I'll try you again. Suppose you were going to carpet a room. Would you use a carpet having a representation of flowers upon it?"

There being a general conviction by this time that "No, sir!" was always the right answer to this gentleman, the chorus of No was very strong. Only a few feeble stragglers said Yes; among them Sissy Jupe.

"Girl number twenty," said the gentleman, smiling in the calm strength of knowledge.

Sissy blushed, and stood up.

"So you would carpet your room—or your husband's room, if you were a grown woman, and had a husband—with representations of flowers, would you?" said the gentleman. "Why would you?"

"If you please, sir, I am very fond of flowers," returned the girl.

"And is that why you would put tables and chairs upon them, and have people walking over them with heavy boots?"

"It wouldn't hurt them, sir. They wouldn't crush and wither, if you please, sir. They would be the pictures of what was very pretty and pleasant, and I would fancy—"

"Ay, ay, ay! But you mustn't fancy," cried the gentleman, quite elated by coming so happily to his point. "That's it! You are never to fancy."

"You are not, Cecilia Jupe," Thomas Gradgrind solemnly repeated, "to do anything of that kind."

"Fact, fact, fact!" said the gentleman. And "Fact, fact, fact!" repeated Thomas Gradgrind.

"You are to be in all things regulated and governed," said the gentleman, "by fact. We hope to have, before long, a board of fact, composed of commissioners of fact, who will force the people to be a people of fact, and of nothing but fact. You must discard the word Fancy altogether. You have nothing to do with it. You are not to have, in any object of use or ornament, what would be a contradiction in fact. You don't walk upon flowers in fact; you cannot be allowed to walk upon flowers in carpets. You don't find that foreign birds and butterflies come and perch upon your crockery; you cannot be permitted to paint foreign birds and butterflies upon your crockery. You never meet with quadrupeds going up and down walls; you must not have quadrupeds represented upon walls. You must use," said the gentleman, "for all these purposes, combinations and modification (in primary colours) of mathematical figures which are susceptible of proof and demonstration. This is the new discovery. This is fact. This is taste."

The girl curtsied, and sat down. She was very young, and she looked as if she were frightened by the matter of fact prospect the world afforded.

"Now, if Mr. M'Choakumchild," said the gentleman, "will proceed to give his first lesson here, Mr. Gradgrind, I shall be happy, at your request, to observe his mode of procedure."

Mr. Gradgrind was much obliged. "Mr. M'Choakumchild, we only wait for you."

So Mr. M'Choakumchild began in his best manner. He and some one hundred and forty other schoolmasters had been lately turned at the same time, in the same factory, on the same principles, like so many pianoforte legs. He had been put through an immense variety of paces, and had answered volumes of head-breaking questions. Orthography, etymology, syntax, and prosody, biography, astronomy, geography, and general cosmography, the sciences of compound proportion, algebra, land-surveying and levelling, vocal music, and drawing from models, were all at the ends of his ten chilled fingers. He had worked his stony way into Her Majesty's most Honourable Privy Council's Schedule B, and had taken the bloom off the higher branches of mathematics and physical science, French, German, Latin, and Greek. He knew all about the Watersheds of all the world (whatever they are), and all the histories of all the peoples, and all the names of all the rivers and mountains, and all the productions, manners, and customs of all the countries, and all their boundaries and bearings on the two and thirty points of the compass. Ah, rather overdone, M'Choakumchild. If he had only learnt a little less, how infinitely better he might have taught much more!

He went to work in this preparatory lesson, not unlike Morgiana in the Forty Thieves—looking into all the vessels ranged before him, one after another, to see what they contained. Say, good M'Choakumchild: when from thy boiling store thou shalt fill each jar brim full by-and-by, dost thou think that thou wilt always kill outright the robber Fancy lurking within—or sometimes only maim him and distort him!

LITERATURE AND SCIENCE

Matthew Arnold

The usual education in the past has been mainly literary. The question is whether the studies which were long supposed to be the best for all of us are practically the best now; whether others are not better. The tyranny of the past, many think, weighs on us injuriously in the predominance given to letters in education. The question is raised whether, to meet the needs of our modern life, the predominance ought not now to pass from letters to science; and naturally the question is nowhere raised with more energy than here in the United States. The design of abasing what is called 'mere literary instruction and education,' and of exalting what is called 'sound, extensive, and practical scientific knowledge,' is, in this intensely modern world of the United States, even more perhaps than in Europe, a very popular design, and makes great and rapid progress.

I am going to ask whether the present movement for ousting letters from their old predominance in education, and for transferring the predominance in education to the natural sciences, whether this brisk and flourishing movement ought to prevail, and whether it is likely that in the end it really will prevail.

Some of you may possibly remember a phrase of mine which has been the object of a good deal of comment; an observation to the effect that in our culture, the aim being *to know ourselves and the world*, we have, as the means to this end, *to know the best which has been thought and said in the world*. A man of science, who is also an excellent writer and the very

prince of debaters, Professor Huxley, in a discourse at the
opening of Sir Josiah Mason's college at Birmingham, laying
hold of this phrase, expanded it by quoting some more words
of mine, which are these: 'The civilised world is to be regarded
as now being, for intellectual and spiritual purposes, one great
confederation, bound to a joint action and working to a common result; and whose members have for their proper outfit
a knowledge of Greek, Roman, and Eastern antiquity, and of
one another. Special local and temporary advantages being put
out of account, that modern nation will in the intellectual and
spiritual sphere make most progress, which most thoroughly
carries out this programme.'

Now on my phrase, thus enlarged, Professor Huxley remarks
that when I speak of the above-mentioned knowledge as
enabling us to know ourselves and the world, I assert *literature*
to contain the materials which suffice for thus making us know
ourselves and the world. But it is not by any means clear, says
he, that after having learnt all which ancient and modern
literatures have to tell us, we have laid a sufficiently broad
and deep foundation for that criticism of life, that knowledge
of ourselves and the world, which constitutes culture. On the
contrary, Professor Huxley declares that he finds himself
'wholly unable to admit that either nations or individuals will
really advance, if their outfit draws nothing from the stores
of physical science. An army without weapons of precision, and
with no particular base of operations, might more hopefully
enter upon a campaign on the Rhine, than a man, devoid of
a knowledge of what physical science has done in the last
century, upon a criticism of life.'

This shows how needful it is for those who are to discuss
any matter together, to have a common understanding as to
the sense of the terms they employ,—how needful, and how
difficult. What Professor Huxley says, implies just the reproach
which is so often brought against the study of *belles lettres*,
as they are called: that the study is an elegant one, but slight
and ineffectual; a smattering of Greek and Latin and other
ornamental things, of little use for any one whose object is
to get at truth, and to be a practical man. So, too, M. Renan
talks of the 'superficial humanism' of a school-course which

treats us as if we were all going to be poets, writers, preachers, orators, and he opposes this humanism to positive science, or the critical search after truth. And there is always a tendency in those who are remonstrating against the predominance of letters in education, to understand by letters *belles lettres*, and by *belles lettres* a superficial humanism, the opposite of science or true knowledge.

But when we talk of knowing Greek and Roman antiquity, for instance, which is the knowledge people have called the humanities, I for my part mean a knowledge which is something more than a superficial humanism, mainly decorative. 'I call all teaching *scientific*,' says Wolf, the critic of Homer, 'which is systematically laid out and followed up to its original sources. For example: a knowledge of classical antiquity is scientific when the remains of classical antiquity are correctly studied in the original languages.' There can be no doubt that Wolf is perfectly right; that all learning is scientific which is systematically laid out and followed up to its original sources, and that a genuine humanism is scientific.

Let us, I say, be agreed about the meaning of the terms we are using. I talk of knowing the best which has been thought and uttered in the world; Professor Huxley says this means knowing *literature*. Literature is a large word; it may mean everything written with letters or printed in a book. Euclid's *Elements* and Newton's *Principia* are thus literature. All knowledge that reaches us through books is literature. But by literature Professor Huxley means *belles lettres*. He means to make me say, that knowing the best which has been thought and said by the modern nations is knowing their *belles lettres* and no more. And this is no sufficient equipment, he argues, for a criticism of modern life. But as I do not mean, by knowing ancient Rome, knowing merely more or less of Latin *belles lettres*, and taking no account of Rome's military, and political, and legal, and administrative work in the world; and as, by knowing ancient Greece, I understand knowing her as the giver of Greek art, and the guide to a free and right use of reason and to scientific method, and the founder of our mathematics and physics and astronomy and biology,— I understand knowing her as all this, and not merely knowing

certain Greek poems, and histories, and treatises, and speeches,
—so as to the knowledge of modern nations also. By knowing
modern nations, I mean not merely knowing their *belles
lettres*, but knowing also what has been done by such men as
Copernicus, Galileo, Newton, Darwin. 'Our ancestors learned,'
says Professor Huxley, 'that the earth is the centre of the
visible universe, and that man is the cynosure of things
terrestrial; and more especially was it inculcated that the course
of nature had no fixed order, but that it could be, and constantly was, altered.' But for us now, continues Professor
Huxley, 'the notions of the beginning and the end of the
world entertained by our forefathers are no longer credible.
It is very certain that the earth is not the chief body in the
material universe, and that the world is not subordinated to
man's use. It is even more certain that nature is the expression
of a definite order, with which nothing interferes.' 'And yet,'
he cries, 'the purely classical education advocated by the
representatives of the humanists in our day gives no inkling
of all this!'

At present the question is as to what is meant by knowing
the best which modern nations have thought and said. It is
not knowing their *belles lettres* merely which is meant. To
know Italian *belles lettres* is not to know Italy, and to know
English *belles lettres* is not to know England. Into knowing
Italy and England there comes a great deal more, Galileo and
Newton amongst it. The reproach of being a superficial
humanism, a tincture of *belles lettres*, may attach rightly
enough to some other disciplines; but to the particular discipline recommended when I proposed knowing the best that
has been thought and said in the world, it does not apply. In
that best I certainly include what in modern times has been
thought and said by the great observers and knowers of nature.

There is, therefore, really no question between Professor
Huxley and me as to whether knowing the great results of
the modern scientific study of nature is not required as a part
of our culture, as well as knowing the products of literature and
art. But to follow the processes by which those results are
reached, ought, say the friends of physical science, to be made
the staple of education for the bulk of mankind. And here

there does arise a question between those whom Professor
Huxley calls with playful sarcasm 'the Levites of culture,' and
those whom the poor humanist is sometimes apt to regard
as its Nebuchadnezzars.

The great results of the scientific investigation of nature we
are agreed upon knowing, but how much of our study are we
bound to give to the processes by which those results are
reached? The results have their visible bearing on human life.
But all the processes, too, all the items of fact, by which those
results are reached and established, are interesting. All knowledge is interesting to a wise man, and the knowledge of nature
is interesting to all men. It is very interesting to know, that,
from the albuminous white of the egg, the chick in the egg
gets the materials for its flesh, bones, blood, and feathers;
while, from the fatty yolk of the egg, it gets the heat and
energy which enable it at length to break its shell and begin
the world. It is less interesting, perhaps, but still it is interesting, to know that when a taper burns, the wax is converted
into carbonic acid and water. Moreover, it is quite true that
the habit of dealing with facts, which is given by the study of
nature, is, as friends of physical science praise it for being, an
excellent discipline. The appeal, in the study of nature, is
constantly to observation and experiment; not only is it said
that the thing is so, but we can be made to see that it is so.
We must all admit that in natural science the habit gained of
dealing with facts is a most valuable discipline, and that every
one should have some experience of it.

More than this, however, is demanded by the reformers. It
is proposed to make the training in natural science the main
part of education, for the great majority of mankind at any
rate. And here, I confess, I part company with the friends of
physical science, with whom up to this point I have been
agreeing. In differing from them, however, I wish to proceed
with the utmost caution and diffidence. The smallness of my
own acquaintance with the disciplines of natural science is
ever before my mind, and I am fearful of doing these disciplines
an injustice. The ability and pugnacity of the partisans of natural science make them formidable persons to contradict. The
tone of tentative inquiry, which befits a being of dim faculties

and bounded knowledge, is the tone I would wish to take and not to depart from. At present it seems to me, that those who are for giving to natural knowledge, as they call it, the chief place in the education of the majority of mankind, leave one important thing out of their account: the constitution of human nature. But I put this forward on the strength of some facts not at all recondite, very far from it; facts capable of being stated in the simplest possible fashion, and to which, if I so state them, the man of science will, I am sure, be willing to allow their due weight.

Deny the facts altogether, I think, he hardly can. He can hardly deny, that when we set ourselves to enumerate the powers which go to the building up of human life, and say that they are the power of conduct, the power of intellect and knowledge, the power of beauty, and the power of social life and manners,—he can hardly deny that this scheme, though drawn in rough and plain lines enough, and not pretending to scientific exactness, does yet give a fairly true representation of the matter. Human nature is built up by these powers; we have the need for them all. When we have rightly met and adjusted the claims of them all, we shall then be in a fair way for getting soberness and righteousness, with wisdom. This is evident enough, and the friends of physical science would admit it.

But perhaps they may not have sufficiently observed another thing: namely, that the several powers just mentioned are not isolated, but there is, in the generality of mankind, a perpetual tendency to relate them one to another in divers ways. With one such way of relating them I am particularly concerned now. Following our instinct for intellect and knowledge, we acquire pieces of knowledge; and presently, in the generality of men, there arises the desire to relate these pieces of knowledge to our sense for conduct, to our sense for beauty,—and there is weariness and dissatisfaction if the desire is baulked. Now in this desire lies, I think, the strength of that hold which letters have upon us.

But, no doubt, some kinds of knowledge cannot be made to directly serve the instinct in question, cannot be directly related to the sense for beauty, to the sense for conduct. These are instrument-knowledges; they lead on to other knowledges, which can. A man who passes his life in instrument-knowledges is a specialist. They may be invaluable as instruments to something beyond, for those who have the gift thus to employ them; and they may be disciplines in themselves wherein it is useful for every one to have some schooling. But it is inconceivable that the generality of men should pass all their mental life with Greek accents or with formal logic. My friend Professor Sylvester, who is one of the first mathematicians in the world, holds transcendental doctrines as to the virtue of mathematics, but those doctrines are not for common men. In the very Senate House and heart of our English Cambridge I once ventured, though not without an apology for my profaneness, to hazard the opinion that for the majority of mankind a little of mathematics, even, goes a long way. Of course this is quite consistent with their being of immense importance as an instrument to something else; but it is the few who have the aptitude for thus using them, not the bulk of mankind.

The natural sciences do not, however, stand on the same footing with these instrument-knowledges. Experience shows us that the generality of men will find more interest in learning that, when a taper burns, the wax is converted into carbonic acid and water, or in learning the explanation of the phenomenon of dew, or in learning how the circulation of the blood is carried on, than they find in learning that the genitive plural of *pais* and *pas* does not take the circumflex on the termination. And one piece of natural knowledge is added to another, and others are added to that, and at last we come to propositions so interesting as Mr. Darwin's famous proposition that 'our ancestor was a hairy quadruped furnished with a tail and pointed ears, probably arboreal in his habits.' Or we come to propositions of such reach and magnitude as those which Professor Huxley delivers, when he says that the notions of our forefathers about the beginning and the end of the world were all wrong, and that nature is the expression of a definite order with which nothing interferes.

Interesting, indeed, these results of science are, important they are, and we should all of us be acquainted with them. But what I now wish you to mark is, that we are still, when they are propounded to us and we receive them, we are still in the sphere of intellect and knowledge. And for the generality of men there will be found, I say, to arise, when they have duly taken in the proposition that their ancestor was 'a hairy quadruped furnished with a tail and pointed ears, probably arboreal in his habits,' there will be found to arise an invincible desire to relate this proposition to the sense in us for conduct, and to the sense in us for beauty. But this the men of science will not do for us, and will hardly even profess to do. They will give us other pieces of knowledge, other facts, about other animals and their ancestors, or about plants, or about stones, or about stars; and they may finally bring us to those great 'general conceptions of the universe which are forced upon us all,' says Professor Huxley, 'by the progress of physical science.' But still it will be *knowledge* only which they give us; knowledge not put for us into relation with our sense for conduct, our sense for beauty, and touched with emotion by being so put; not thus put for us, and therefore, to the majority of mankind, after a certain while, unsatisfying, wearying.

Not to the born naturalist, I admit. But what do we mean by a born naturalist? We mean a man in whom the zeal for observing nature is so uncommonly strong and eminent, that it marks him off from the bulk of mankind. Such a man will pass his life happily in collecting natural knowledge and reasoning upon it, and will ask for nothing, or hardly anything, more. I heard it said that the sagacious and admirable naturalist whom we lost not very long ago, Mr. Darwin, once owned to a friend that for his part he did not experience the necessity for two things which most men find so necessary to them,— religion and poetry; science and the domestic affections, he thought, were enough. To a born naturalist, I can well understand that this should seem so. So absorbing is his occupation with nature, so strong his love for his occupation, that he goes on acquiring natural knowledge and reasoning upon it, and has little time or inclination for thinking about getting it related to the desire in man for conduct, the desire in man for beauty. He relates it to them for himself as he goes along, so far as he feels the need; and he draws from the domestic affections all the additional solace necessary. But then Darwins are extremely rare. Another great and admirable master of natural knowledge, Faraday, was a Sandemanian. That is to say, he related his knowledge to his instinct for conduct and to his instinct for beauty, by the aid of that respectable Scottish sectary, Robert Sandeman. And so strong, in general, is the demand of religion and poetry to have their share in a man, to associate themselves with his knowing, and to relieve and rejoice it, that, probably, for one man amongst us with the disposition to do as Darwin did in this respect, there are at least fifty with the disposition to do as Faraday.

SCIENCE AND CULTURE

Thomas Henry Huxley

From the time that the first suggestion to introduce physical science into ordinary education was timidly whispered, until now, the advocates of scientific education have met with opposition of two kinds. On the one hand, they have been pooh-poohed by the men of business who pride themselves on being the representatives of practicality; while, on the other hand, they have been excommunicated by the classical scholars, in their capacity of Levites in charge of the ark of culture and monopolists of liberal education.

The practical men believed that the idol whom they worship—rule of thumb—has been the source of the past prosperity, and will suffice for the future welfare of the arts and manufactures. They are of opinion that science is speculative rubbish; that theory and practice have nothing to do with one another; and that the scientific habit of mind is an impediment, rather than an aid, in the conduct of ordinary affairs.

I have used the past tense in speaking of the practical men— for although they were very formidable thirty years ago, I am

Delivered as an address at the opening of a Scientific College at Birmingham, England, which had been endowed by Sir Josiah Mason, a self-made businessman.

not sure that the pure species has not been extirpated. In fact, so far as mere argument goes, they have been subjected to such a *feu d'enfer* [1] that it is a miracle if any have escaped. But I have remarked that your typical practical man has an unexpected resemblance to one of Milton's angels. His spiritual wounds, such as are inflicted by logical weapons, may be as deep as a well and as wide as a church door, but beyond shedding a few drops of ichor, celestial or otherwise, he is no whit the worse. So, if any of these opponents be left, I will not waste time in vain repetition of the demonstrative evidence of the practical value of science; but knowing that a parable will sometimes penetrate where syllogisms fail to effect an entrance, I will offer a story for their consideration.

Once upon a time, a boy, with nothing to depend upon but his own vigorous nature, was thrown into the thick of the struggle for existence in the midst of a great manufacturing population. He seems to have had a hard fight, inasmuch as, by the time he was thirty years of age, his total disposable funds amounted to twenty pounds. Nevertheless, middle life found him giving proof of his comprehension of the practical problems he had been roughly called upon to solve, by a career of remarkable prosperity.

Finally, having reached old age with its well-earned surroundings of 'honour, troops of friends,' the hero of my story bethought himself of those who were making a like start in life, and how he could stretch out a helping hand to them.

After long and anxious reflection this successful practical man of business could devise nothing better than to provide them with the means of obtaining 'sound, extensive, and practical scientific knowledge.' And he devoted a large part of his wealth and five years of incessant work to this end.

I need not point the moral of a tale which, as the solid and spacious fabric of the Scientific College assures us, is no fable, nor can anything which I could say intensify the force of this practical answer to practical objections.

We may take it for granted then, that, in the opinion of those best qualified to judge, the diffusion of thorough scien-

[1] Hell-fire.

tific education is an absolutely essential condition of industrial progress; and that the College which has been opened today will confer an inestimable boon upon those whose livelihood is to be gained by the practise of the arts and manufactures of the district.

The only question worth discussion is, whether the conditions, under which the work of the College is to be carried out, are such as to give it the best possible chance of achieving permanent success.

Sir Josiah Mason, without doubt most wisely, has left very large freedom of action to the trustees, to whom he proposes ultimately to commit the administration of the College, so that they may be able to adjust its arrangements in accordance with the changing conditions of the future. But, with respect to three points, he has laid most explicit injunctions upon both administrators and teachers.

Party politics are forbidden to enter into the minds of either, so far as the work of the College is concerned; theology is as sternly banished from its precincts; and finally, it is especially declared that the College shall make no provision for 'mere literary instruction and education.'

It does not concern me at present to dwell upon the first two injunctions any longer than may be needful to express my full conviction of their wisdom. But the third prohibition brings us face to face with those other opponents of scientific education, who are by no means in the moribund condition of the practical man, but alive, alert, and formidable.

It is not impossible that we shall hear this express exclusion if 'literary instruction and education' from a College which, nevertheless, professes to give a high and efficient education, sharply criticised. Certainly the time was that the Levites of culture would have sounded their trumpets against its walls as against an educational Jericho.

How often have we not been told that the study of physical science is incompetent to confer culture; that it touches none of the higher problems of life; and, what is worse, that the continual devotion to scientific studies tends to generate a narrow and bigoted belief in the applicability of scientific methods to the search after truth of all kinds? How frequently

one has reason to observe that no reply to a troublesome argument tells so well as calling its author a 'mere scientific specialist.' And, as I am afraid it is not permissible to speak of this
form of opposition to scientific education in the past tense;
may we not expect to be told that this, not only omission,
but prohibition, of 'mere literary instruction and education'
is a patent example of scientific narrow-mindedness?

I am not acquainted with Sir Josiah Mason's reasons for the
action which he has taken; but if, as I apprehend is the case,
he refers to the ordinary classical course of our schools and
universities by the name of 'mere literary instruction and education,' I venture to offer sundry reasons of my own in support
of that action.

For I hold very strongly by two convictions: The first is,
that neither the discipline nor the subject-matter of classical
education is of such direct value to the student of physical
science as to justify the expenditure of valuable time upon
either; and the second is, that for the purpose of attaining real
culture, an exclusively scientific education is at least as effectual
as an exclusively literary education.

I need hardly point out to you that these opinions, especially
the latter, are diametrically opposed to those of the great majority of educated Englishmen, influenced as they are by school
and university traditions. In their belief, culture is obtainable
only by a liberal education; and a liberal education is synony-
mous, not merely with education and instruction in literature,
but in one particular form of literature, namely, that of Greek
and Roman antiquity. They hold that the man who has learned
Latin and Greek, however little, is educated; while he who is
versed in other branches of knowledge, however deeply, is a
more or less respectable specialist, not admissible into the
cultured caste. The stamp of the educated man, the University
degree, is not for him.

I am too well acquainted with the generous catholicity of
spirit, the true sympathy with scientific thought, which per-
vades the writings of our chief apostle of culture [2] to identify

---

[2] Matthew Arnold; "epistles to the Philistines" is an allusion to his
essays urging culture upon complacement materialists, whom he termed
Philistines. Arnold's "Literature and Science" is a response to Huxley's
arguments.

him with these opinions; and yet one may cull from one and another of those epistles to the Philistines, which so much delight all who do not answer to that name, sentences which lend them some support.

Mr. Arnold tells us that the meaning of culture is 'to know the best that has been thought and said in the world.' It is the criticism of life contained in literature. That criticism regards 'Europe as being, for intellectual and spiritual purposes, one great confederation, bound to a joint action and working to a common result; and whose members have, for their common outfit, a knowledge of Greek, Roman, and Eastern antiquity, and of one another. Special, local, and temporary advantages being put out of account, that modern nation will in the intellectual and spiritual sphere make most progress, which most thoroughly carries out this programme. And what is that but saying that we too, all of us, as individuals, the more thoroughly we carry it out, shall make the more progress?'

We have here to deal with two distinct propositions. The first, that a criticism of life is the essence of culture; the second, that literature contains the materials which suffice for the construction of such criticism.

I think that we must all assent to the first proposition. For culture certainly means something quite different from learning or technical skill. It implies the possession of an ideal, and the habit of critically estimating the value of things by comparison with a theoretic standard. Perfect culture should supply a complete theory of life, based upon a clear knowledge alike of its possibilities and of its limitations.

But we may agree to all this, and yet strongly dissent from the assumption that literature alone is competent to supply this knowledge. After having learnt all that Greek, Roman, and Eastern antiquity have thought and said, and all that modern literature have to tell us, it is not self-evident that we have laid a sufficiently broad and deep foundation for that criticism of life, which constitutes culture.

Indeed, to any one acquainted with the scope of physical science, it is not at all evident. Considering progress only in the 'intellectual and spiritual sphere,' I find myself wholly unable to admit that either nations or individuals will really advance, if their common outfit draws nothing from the stores of physical science. I should say that an army, without weapons of precision and with no particular base of operations, might more hopefully enter upon a campaign on the Rhine, than a man, devoid of a knowledge of what physical science has done in the last century, upon a criticism of life.

When a biologist meets with an anomaly, he instinctively turns to the study of development to clear it up. The rationale of contradictory opinions may with equal confidence be sought in history.

It is, happily, no new thing that Englishmen should employ their wealth in building and endowing institutions for educational purposes. But, five or six hundred years ago, deeds of foundation expressed or implied conditions as nearly as possible contrary to those which have been thought expedient by Sir Josiah Mason. That is to say, physical science was practically ignored, while a certain literary training was enjoined as a means to the acquirement of knowledge which was essentially theological.

The reason of this singular contradiction between the actions of men alike animated by a strong and disinterested desire to promote the welfare of their fellows, is easily discovered.

At that time, in fact, if any one desired knowledge beyond such as could be obtained by his own observation, or by common conversation, his first necessity was to learn the Latin language, inasmuch as all the higher knowledge of the western world was contained in works written in that language. Hence, Latin grammar, with logic and rhetoric, studied through Latin, were the fundamentals of education. With respect to the substance of the knowledge imparted through this channel, the Jewish and Christian Scriptures, as interpreted and supplemented by the Romish Church, were held to contain a complete and infallibly true body of information.

Theological dicta were, to the thinkers of those days, that which the axioms and definitions of Euclid are to the geometers of these. The business of the philosophers of the middle ages was to deduce from the data furnished by the theologians, conclusions in accordance with ecclesiastical decrees. They were allowed the high privilege of showing, by logical process, how and why that which the Church said was true, must be true. And if their demonstrations fell short of or exceeded this limit, the Church was maternally ready to check their aberrations; if need were, by the help of the secular arm.

Between the two, our ancestors were furnished with a compact and complete criticism of life. They were told how the world began and how it would end; they learned that all material existence was but a base and insignificant blot upon the fair face of the spiritual world, and that nature was, to all intents and purposes, the playground of the devil; they learned that the earth is the centre of the visible universe, and that man is the cynosure of things terrestrial, and more especially was it inculcated that the course of nature had no fixed order, but that it could be, and constantly was, altered by the agency of innumerable spiritual beings, good and bad, according as they were moved by the deeds and prayers of men. The sum and substance of the whole doctrine was to produce the conviction that the only thing really worth knowing in this world was how to secure that place in a better which, under certain conditions, the Church promised.

Our ancestors had a living belief in this theory of life, and acted upon it in their dealings with education, as in all other matters. Culture meant saintliness—after the fashion of the saints of those days; the education that led to it was, of necessity, theological; and the way to theology lay through Latin.

That the study of nature—further than was requisite for the satisfaction of everyday wants—should have any bearing on human life was far from the thoughts of men thus trained. Indeed, as nature had been cursed for man's sake, it was an obvious conclusion that those who meddled with nature were likely to come into pretty close contact with Satan. And, if any born scientific investigator followed his instincts, he might safely reckon upon earning the reputation, and probably upon suffering the fate, of a sorcerer.

Had the western world been left to itself in Chinese isolation, there is no saying how long this state of things might have endured. But, happily, it was not left to itself. Even earlier than the thirteenth century, the development of Moorish civilisation

in Spain and the great movement of the Crusades had introduced the leaven which, from that day to this, has never ceased
to work. At first, through the intermediation of Arabic trans-
lations, afterwards by the study of the originals, the western
nations of Europe became acquainted with the writings of the
ancient philosophers and poets, and, in time, with the whole
of the vast literature of antiquity.

Whatever there was of high intellectual aspiration or dom-
inant capacity in Italy, France, Germany, and England, spent
itself for centuries in taking possession of the rich inheritance
left by the dead civilisations of Greece and Rome. Marvellously
aided by the invention of printing, classical learning spread and
flourished. Those who possessed it prided themselves on having
attained the highest culture then within the reach of mankind.

And justly. For, saving Dante on his solitary pinnacle, there
was no figure in modern literature at the time of the Renascence to compare with the men of antiquity; there was no art
to compete with their sculpture; there was no physical science
but that which Greece had created. Above all, there was no
other example of perfect intellectual freedom—of the un-
hesitating acceptance of reason as the sole guide to truth and
the supreme arbiter of conduct.

The new learning necessarily soon exerted a profound influence upon education. The language of the monks and school-
men seemed little better than gibberish to scholars fresh from
Virgil and Cicero, and the study of Latin was placed upon a
new foundation. Moreover, Latin itself ceased to afford the
sole key to knowledge. The student who sought the highest
thought of antiquity, found only a second-hand reflection of
it in Roman literature, and turned his face to the full light of
the Greeks. And after a battle, not altogether dissimilar to
that which is at present being fought over the teaching of
physical science, the study of Greek was recognised as an
essential element of all higher education.

Then the Humanists, as they were called, won the day; and
the great reform which they effected was of incalculable service
to mankind. But the Nemesis of all reformers is finality; and
the reformers of education, like those of religion, fell into the
profound, however common, error of mistaking the beginning

for the end of the work of reformation.

The representatives of the Humanists, in the nineteenth century, take their stand upon classical education as the sole avenue to culture, as firmly as if we were still in the age of Renascence. Yet, surely, the present intellectual relations of the modern and the ancient worlds are profoundly different from those which obtained three centuries ago. Leaving aside the existence of a great and characteristically modern literature, of modern painting, and, especially, of modern music, there is one feature of the present state of the civilised world which separates it more widely from the Renascence, than the Renascence was separated from the middle ages.

This distinctive character of our own times lies in the vast and constantly increasing part which is played by natural knowledge. Not only is our daily life shaped by it; not only does the prosperity of millions of men depend upon it, but our whole theory of life has long been influenced, consciously or unconsciously, by the general conceptions of the universe, which have been forced upon us by physical science.

In fact, the most elementary acquaintance with the results of scientific investigation shows us that they offer a broad and striking contradiction to the opinion so implicitly credited and taught in the middle ages.

The notions of the beginning and the end of the world entertained by our forefathers are no longer credible. It is very certain that the earth is not the chief body in the material universe, and that the world is not subordinated to man's use. It is even more certain that nature is the expression of a definite order with which nothing interferes, and that the chief business of mankind is to learn that order and govern themselves accordingly. Moreover this scientific 'criticism of life' presents itself to us with different credentials from any other. It appeals not to authority, nor to what anybody may have thought or said, but to nature. It admits that all our interpretations of natural fact are more or less imperfect and symbolic, and bits the learned seek for truth not among words but among things. It warns us that the assertion which outstrips evidence is not only a blunder but a crime.

The purely classical education advocated by the representatives of the Humanists in our day, gives no inkling of all this. A man may be a better scholar than Erasmus, and know no more of the chief causes of the present intellectual fermentation than Erasmus did. Scholarly and pious persons, worthy of all respect, favour us with allocutions upon the sadness of the antagonism of science to their mediæval way of thinking, which betray an ignorance of the first principles of scientific investigation, an incapacity for understanding what a man of science means by veracity, and an unconsciousness of the weight of established scientific truths, which is almost comical. . . .

Thus I venture to think that the pretensions of our modern Humanists to the possession of the monopoly of culture and to the exclusive inheritance of the spirit of antiquity must be abated, if not abandoned. But I should be very sorry that anything I have said should be taken to imply a desire on my part to depreciate the value of classical education, as it might be and as it sometimes is. The native capacities of mankind vary no less than their opportunities; and while culture is one, the road by which one man may best reach it is widely different from that which is most advantageous to another. Again, while scientific education is yet inchoate and tentative, classical education is thoroughly well organised upon the practical experience of generations of teachers. So that, given ample time for learning and estimation for ordinary life, or for a literary career, I do not think that a young Englishman in search of culture can do better than follow the course usually marked out for him, supplementing its deficiencies by his own efforts.

But for those who mean to make science their serious occupation; or who intend to follow the profession of medicine; or who have to enter early upon the business of life; for all these, in my opinion, classical education is a mistake; and it is for this reason that I am glad to see 'mere literary education and instruction' shut out from the curriculum of Sir Josiah Mason's College, seeing that its inclusion would probably lead to the introduction of the ordinary smattering of Latin and Greek.

Nevertheless, I am the last person to question the importance of genuine literary education, or to suppose that intellectual culture can be complete without it. An exclusively scientific training will bring about a mental twist as surely as an exclusively literary training. The value of the cargo does not compensate for a ship's being out of trim; and I should be very sorry to think that the Scientific College would turn out none but lopsided men.

There is no need, however, that such a catastrophe should happen. Instruction in English, French, and German is provided, and thus the three greatest literatures of the modern world are made accessible to the student.

French and German, and especially the latter language, are absolutely indispensable to those who desire full knowledge in any department of science. But even supposing that the knowledge of these languages acquired is not more than sufficient for purely scientific purposes, every Englishman has, in his native tongue, an almost perfect instrument of literary expression; and, in his own literature, models of every kind of literary excellence. If an Englishman cannot get literary culture out of his Bible, his Shakespeare, his Milton, neither, in my belief, will the profoundest study of Homer and Sophocles, Virgil and Horace, give it to him.

Thus, since the constitution of the College makes sufficient provision for literary as well as for scientific education, and since artistic instruction is also contemplated, it seems to me that a fairly complete culture is offered to all who are willing to take advantage of it.

SCIENCE, LITERATURE & CULTURE:
A Comment on the Leavis-Snow
Controversy

Lionel Trilling

It is now nearly eighty years since Matthew Arnold came to this country on his famous lecture tour. Of his repertory of three lectures, none was calculated to give unqualified pleasure to his audience. The lecture on Emerson praised that most eminent of American writers only after it had denied that he was a literary figure of the first order. The lecture called "Numbers" raised disturbing questions about the relation of democracy to excellence and distinction. "Literature and Science" was the least likely to give offense, yet even this most memorable of the three *Discourses in America* was not without its touch of uncomfortableness. In 1883 America was by no means committed —and, indeed, never was to be committed—to the belief that the right education for the modern age must be predominantly scientific and technical, and Arnold, when he cited the proponents of this idea, which of course he opposed, mentioned only those who were English. Yet his audiences surely knew that Arnold was warning them against what would seem to be the natural tendency of an industrial democracy to devalue the old "aristocratic" education in favor of studies that are merely practical.

Arnold wrote "Emerson" and "Numbers" especially for his American tour, but he had first composed "Literature and Science" as the Rede Lecture at Cambridge in 1882. Its original occasion cannot fail to have a peculiar interest at this moment, for C. P. Snow's *The Two Cultures and the Scientific Revolu-*

From *Commentary* (June, 1962), pp. 461–77. Reprinted by permission of *Commentary* and Lionel Trilling.

tion, around which so curious a storm rages in England, was the Rede Lecture of 1959.

Sir Charles did not mention his great predecessor in the lectureship, although his own discourse was exactly on Arnold's subject and took a line exactly the opposite of Arnold's. And F. R. Leavis, whose admiration of Arnold is well known and whose position in respect to the relative importance of literature and of science in education is much the same as Arnold's, did not mention Arnold either, when, in his recent Richmond Lecture at Downing College, he launched an attack of unexampled ferocity upon the doctrine and the author of *The Two Cultures.*

In its essential terms, the issue in debate has not changed since Arnold spoke. Arnold's chief antagonist was T. H. Huxley —it was he who, in his lecture on "Culture and Education," had said that literature should, and inevitably would, step down from its preeminent place in education, that science and not "culture" must supply the knowledge which is necessary for an age committed to rational truth and material practicality. What is more, Huxley said, science will supply the very basis of the assumptions of modern ethics. In effect Snow says nothing different.

The word "culture" had been Arnold's personal insigne ever since the publication of *Culture and Anarchy* in 1867 and Huxley made particular reference to the views on the value of humanistic study which Arnold had expressed in that book.[1] Arnold's reply in "Literature and Science" could not have been simpler, just as it could not have been more temperate, although it surely did not surpass in temperateness Huxley's statement of his disagreement with Arnold's ideas; the two men held each other in high admiration and were warm friends. Arnold said that he had not the least disposition to propose that science be slighted in education. Quite apart from its practical value, scientific knowledge is naturally a delight to the mind, no doubt engaging certain mental temperaments more than others but

---

[1] Arnold, of course, did not use the word in the modern sense in which it is used by anthropologists, sociologists, and historians of thought and art; this is, more or less, the sense in which it is used by Snow. For Arnold, "culture" was "the best that has been thought and said in the world" and also an individual person's relation to this body of thought and expression. My own use of the word in this essay is not Arnold's.

holding out the promise of intellectual pleasure to all. Yet of
itself science does not, as Arnold put it, "serve" the instinct for
conduct and the instinct for beauty, or at least it does not serve
these instincts as they exist in most men. This service, which
includes the relating of scientific knowledge to the whole life of
man, is rendered by culture, which is not to be thought of as
confined to literature—to *belles lettres*—but as comprising all
the humane intellectual disciplines. When Dr. Leavis asserts
the primacy of the humanities in education, he refers more exclusively to literature than Arnold did, but in general effect his
position is the same.

It may seem strange, and a little tiresome, that the debate of
eighty years ago should be instituted again today. Yet it is perhaps understandable in view of the "scientific revolution" about
which Sir Charles tells us. This revolution would seem to be
one of the instances in which a change of quantity becomes a
change in kind—science can now do so much more and do it so
much more quickly than it could a generation ago, let alone in
the last century, that it has been transmuted from what the
world has hitherto known. One of the consequences of this
change—to Sir Charles it is the most salient of all possible consequences—is the new social hope that is now held out to us,
of life made better in material respects, not merely in certain
highly developed countries but all over the world and among
peoples that at the moment are, by Western standards, scarcely
developed at all.

The new power of science perhaps justifies a contemporary
revival of the Victorian question. But if we consent to involve
ourselves in the new dialectic of the old controversy, we must
be aware that we are not addressing ourselves to a question of
educational theory, or to an abstract contention as to what kind
of knowledge has the truest affinity with the human soul. We
approach these matters only to pass through them. What we
address ourselves to is politics, and politics of a quite ultimate
kind, and to the disposition of the modern mind.

II

The Two Cultures has had a very considerable currency in
England and America ever since its publication in 1959, and in

England it was for a time the subject of lively discussion. Indeed, the general agreement in England that it was a statement of great importance, to the point of its being used as an assigned text in secondary schools, was what aroused Dr. Leavis to make his assault on the lecture this long after the first interest in it had subsided. The early discussions of *The Two Cultures* were of a substantive kind, but the concerns which now agitate the English in response to Dr. Leavis's attack have scarcely anything to do with literature and science, or with education, or with social hope. These matters have now been made a mere subordinate element in what amounts to a scandal over a breach of manners. The published comments on Dr. Leavis's attack on *The Two Cultures* were, with few exceptions, directed to such considerations as the exact degree of monstrousness which Dr. Leavis achieved in speaking of Sir Charles as he did; whether or not he spoke out of envy of Sir Charles's reputation; whether or not he has, or deserves to have, any real standing as a critic; or writes acceptable English; or represents, as he claims he does, "the essential Cambridge."

Dr. Leavis's Richmond Lecture, "The Significance of C. P. Snow," was delivered in the Hall of Downing College, Cambridge, on February 28 and published in the *Spectator* of March 9.[2] In the next week's issue of the *Spectator*, seventeen letters appeared, all defending Snow and most of them expressing anger at, or contempt for, Leavis. The following week brought fifteen more communications, of which eight expressed partisanship with Leavis; several of these deplored the tone of the previous week's correspondence. Many of the correspondents who defended Snow were of distinguished reputation; of the defenders of Leavis, the only one known to me was Mr. Geoffrey Wagner, who wrote from America to communicate his belief that the attack on Snow was much needed, for, despite a parody in *New Left Review* in which Snow appears as C. P. Sleet, despite, too, his own adverse criticism of Snow in the *Critic*, "the hosannas obediently continued on this side of the Atlantic, both

[2] In an editorial note, Dr. Leavis is quoted as saying, "The lecture was private and representatives of the press who inquired were informed that there was no admission and that no reporting was to be permitted. The appearance in newspapers of garbled reports has made it desirable that the lecture should appear in full."

from the Barzun-Trilling syndrome and the Book-of-the-Month Club, the worst of both worlds, as it were." Three of the writers of the Snow party touched upon the question of literature and science, the scientist J. D. Bernal, the historian of science Stephen Toulmin, and the literary critic G. S. Fraser. In a miasma of personality-mongering, their letters afforded a degree of relief, but they said little that was of consequence. Of the Leavis party two dons of the University of Birmingham in a joint letter touched rapidly but with some cogency on the relation between literature and science, deploring any attempt to prefer one above the other, concluding that if one must be preferred, it should be, for reasons not stated, literature.

From the *Spectator* letters, so many of them expressing small and rather untidy passions, there are no doubt conclusions to be drawn, of a sufficiently depressing sort, about the condition of cultural life at the moment. But no awareness that we may have of the generally bad state of intellectual affairs ought to blind us to the particular fault of Dr. Leavis in his treatment of Sir Charles Snow. Intelligent and serious himself, Dr. Leavis has in this instance been the cause of stupidity and triviality in other men.

There can be no two opinions about the tone in which Dr. Leavis deals with Sir Charles. It is a bad tone, an impermissible tone. It is bad in a personal sense because it is cruel—it manifestly intends to wound. It is bad intellectually because by its use Dr. Leavis has diverted attention, his own included, from the matter he sought to illuminate. The doctrine of *The Two Cultures* is a momentous one and Dr. Leavis obscures its massive significance by bringing into consideration such matters as Sir Charles's abilities as a novelist, his club membership, his opinion of his own talents, his worldly success, and his relation to worldly power. Anger, scorn, and an excessive consciousness of persons have always been elements of Dr. Leavis's thought— of the very process of his thought, not merely of his manner of expressing it. They were never exactly reassuring elements, but they could be set aside and made to seem of relatively small account in comparison with the remarkable cogency in criticism which Dr. Leavis so often achieved. But as they now appear in his valedictory address—for, in effect, that is what the Richmond Lecture was, since Dr. Leavis retires this year from his university post—they cannot be easily set aside, they stand in the way of what Dr. Leavis means to say.

And, indeed, our understanding of what he means to say is to be derived less from the passionate utterance of the lecture itself than from our knowledge of the whole direction of his career in criticism. That direction was from the first determined by Dr. Leavis's belief that the human faculty above all others to which literature addresses itself is the moral consciousness, which is also the source of all successful creation, the very root of poetic genius. The extent of his commitment to this idea results in what I believe to be a fault in his critical thought—he does not give anything like adequate recognition to those aspects of art which are gratuitous, which arise from high spirits and the impulse to play. One would suppose that the moral consciousness should, for its own purposes, take account of those aspects of art and life that do not fall within its dominion. But if the intensity of Dr. Leavis's commitment to the moral consciousness contrives to produce this deficiency of understanding, it is no less responsible for the accuracy and force which we recognize as the positive characteristics of his work. For Dr. Leavis, literature is what Matthew Arnold said it is, *the criticism of life*—he can understand it in no other way. Both in all its simplicity and in all its hidden complexity, he has made Arnold's saying his own, and from it he has drawn his strength.

If, then, Dr. Leavis now speaks with a very special intensity in response to *The Two Cultures*, we must do him the justice of seeing that the Rede Lecture denies, and in an extreme way, all that he has ever believed about literature—it is, in fact, nothing less than an indictment of literature on social and moral grounds. It represents literature as constituting a danger to the national well-being, and most especially when it is overtly a criticism of life.

Not only because Charles Snow is himself a practitioner of literature but also because he is the man he is, the statement that his lecture has this purport will be shocking and perhaps it will be thought scarcely credible. And I have no doubt that, in another mood and on some other occasion, Sir Charles would

be happy to assert the beneficent powers of literature. But there
can be no other interpretation of his lecture than that it takes
toward literature a position of extreme antagonism.

The Two Cultures begins as an objective statement of the
lack of communication between scientists and literary men.
This is a circumstance that must have been often observed and
often deplored. Perhaps nothing in our culture is so characteristic as the separateness of the various artistic and intellectual
professions. As between, say, poets and painters, or musicians
and architects, there is very little discourse, and perhaps the
same thing could be remarked of scientists of different interests,
say biologists and physicists. But the isolation of literary men
from scientists may well seem to be the most extreme of these
separations, if only because it is the most significant, for a reason
which Sir Charles entirely understands: the especially close
though never clearly defined relation of these two professions
with our social and political life.

The even-handedness with which Sir Charles at first describes
the split between the two "cultures" does not continue for long.
He begins by telling us that scientists and literary men are
equally to blame for the separation—they are kept apart by "a
gulf of mutual incomprehension," by distorted images of each
other which give rise to dislike and hostility. But as Sir Charles's
lecture proceeds, it becomes plain that, although the scientists
do have certain crudities and limitations, they are in general in
the right of things and the literary men in the wrong of them.
The matter which causes the scales to shift thus suddenly is the
human condition. This, Sir Charles tells us, is of its nature
tragic: man dies, and he dies alone. But the awareness of the
ineluctably tragic nature of human life makes a moral trap, "for
it tempts one to sit back, complacent in one's unique tragedy,"
paying no heed to the circumstances of everyday life, which, for
the larger number of human beings, are painful. It is the literary
men, we are told, who are the most likely, the scientists who are
the least likely, to fall into this moral trap; the scientists "are
inclined to be impatient to see if something can be done: and
inclined to think that it can be done, until it's proved otherwise." It is their spirit, "tough and good and determined to fight

it out at the side of their brother men," which has "made scientists regard the other [i.e. the literary] culture's social attitudes as contemptible."

"This is too facile," Sir Charles says in mild rebuke of the scientists, by which he of course means that essentially they are right. There follows a brief consideration of a question raised not by Sir Charles in his own person but by "a scientist of distinction" whom he quotes: "Yeats, Pound, Wyndham Lewis, nine out of ten of those who have dominated literary sensibility in our time, weren't they not only politically silly, but politically wicked? Didn't the influence of all they represent bring Auschwitz that much nearer?" And Sir Charles in answer grants that Yeats was a magnanimous man and a great poet, but he will not, he says, defend the indefensible—"the facts . . . are broadly true." Sir Charles in general agrees, that is, that the literary sensibility of our time brought Auschwitz nearer. He goes on to say that things have changed considerably in the literary life in recent years, even if slowly, for "literature changes more slowly than science."

From the mention of Auschwitz onward, the way is open to the full assertion by Sir Charles of the virtues of the scientists. Although they are admitted to be sometimes gauche or stupidly self-assertive, although Sir Charles concedes of some of them that "the whole literature of the traditional culture doesn't seem relevant to [their] interests" and that, as a result, their "imaginative understanding" is diminished, he yet finds them to be men of a natural decency; they are free from racial feelings, they are lovers of equality, they are cooperative. And chief among their virtues, as Sir Charles describes them, is the fact that they "have the future in their bones."

Indeed, it turns out that it is the future, and not mere ignorance of each other's professional concerns, that makes the separation between the culture of science and the culture of literature. Scientists have the future in their bones. Literary men do not. Quite the contrary—"If the scientists have the future in their bones, then the traditional culture responds by wishing that the future did not exist." The future that the scientists have in their bones is understood to be nothing but a good future; it is very much like the History of the Marxists, which is always the triumph of the right, never possibly the record of defeat. In fact, to entertain the idea that the future might be bad is represented as being tantamount to moral ill-will—in a note appended to the sentence I have just quoted, Sir Charles speaks of George Orwell's 1984 as "the strongest possible wish that the future shall not exist."

It is difficult to credit the implications of this astonishing remark and to ascribe them to Sir Charles. As everyone recalls, Orwell's novel is an imagination of the condition of the world if the authoritarian tendencies which are to be observed in the present develop themselves—logically, as it were—in the future, the point being that it is quite within the range of possibility that this ultimate development should take place. In Orwell's representation of an absolute tyranny, science has a part, and a polemical partisan of science might understand this as the evidence of a literary man's malice toward science. But it is much more likely that, when Orwell imagined science as one of the instruments of repression, he meant to say that science, like everything else that is potentially good, like literature itself, can be perverted and debased to the ends of tyranny. Orwell was a man who, on the basis of actual and painful experience, tried to tell the truth about politics, even his own politics. I believe that he never gave up his commitment to socialism, but he refused to be illusioned in any way he could prevent; it lay within the reach of his mind to conceive that even an idealistic politics, perhaps especially an idealistic politics, can pervert itself. To say of such a man that he wishes that the future—the presumably good future—shall not exist is like saying that intelligence wishes that the future shall not exist.

Having characterized the culture of literature, or, as he sometimes calls it, "the traditional culture," by its hostility to the future, Sir Charles goes on to say that "it is the traditional culture, to an extent remarkably little diminished by the emergence of the scientific one, which manages the western world." This being so, it follows that the traditional culture must be strictly dealt with if the future is to be brought into being: what is called "the existing pattern" must be not merely changed but "broken." Only if this is done shall we be able to educate ourselves as we should. As for the need to educate ourselves: "To say, we have to educate ourselves or perish is perhaps a little more melodramatic than the facts warrant. To say, we have to educate ourselves or watch a steep decline in our lifetime is about right." And Sir Charles indicates our possible fate by the instance—he calls it an "historical myth"—of the Venetian Republic in its last half century. "Its citizens had become rich, as we did, by accident. They had acquired immense political skill, just as we have. A good many of them were tough-minded, realistic, patriotic men. They knew, just as clearly as we know, that the current of history had begun to flow against them. Many of them gave their minds to working out ways to keep going. It would have meant breaking the pattern into which they had been crystallized. They were fond of the pattern, just as we are fond of ours. They never found the will to break it."

I quoted without comment Sir Charles's statement of the idea on which, we may say, the whole argument of *The Two Cultures* is based: "It is the traditional culture, to an extent remarkably little diminished by the emergence of the scientific one, which manages the western world." It is a bewildering statement. In what way can we possibly understand it? That the Western world is managed by some agency which is traditional is of course comprehensible. And we can take in the idea that this agency may be described, for particular purposes of explanation, in terms of a certain set of mind, a general tendency of thought and feeling which, being pervasive, is hard to formulate, and that this is to be called "a culture." But for Sir Charles, the words "traditional" and "literary" are interchangeable, and that this culture, as we agree to call it, is *literary*, that it bears the same relation to actual literary men and their books that what is called the "scientific culture" bears to scientists and their work in laboratories, is truly a staggering thought. The actions of parliaments and congresses and cabinets in directing the massive affairs of state, the negotiations of embassies, the movement of armies and fleets, the establishment of huge scientific projects for the contrivance of armaments and of factories for the production of them, the promises made to citizens, and the choices made by voters at the polls—these, we

are asked to believe, are in the charge of the culture of literature. What can this mean?

It can of course be said that literature has some part in the
management of the Western world, a part which is limited but
perhaps not wholly unimportant. If, for example, we compare
the present condition of industrial England with the condition
of industrial England in the early 19th century, we can say that
the present condition is not, in human respects, anything like
what men of good will might wish it to be, but that it is very
much better than it was in the early years of the Industrial
Revolution. And if we then ask what agencies brought about
the improvement, we can say that one of them was literature.
Certain literary men raised the "Condition of England Question" in a passionate and effective way and their names are still
memorable to us—Coleridge, Carlyle, Mill (I take him to be a
man of letters; he was certainly a good literary critic), Dickens,
Ruskin, Arnold, William Morris. They made their effect only
upon individuals, but the individuals they touched were numerous, and by what they said they made it ever harder for people to be indifferent to the misery around them or to the degradation of the national life in which they came to think
themselves implicated. These literary men helped materially,
some would say decisively, to bring about a change in the state
of affairs. This is not exactly management, but it is a directing
influence such as literature in the modern time often under-
takes to have and sometimes does have.

Yet in Sir Charles's opinion this directing influence of the
literary men of the 19th century deserves no praise. On the contrary, his description of their work is but another count in the
indictment of the culture of literature. Speaking of the response
which literary men made to the Industrial Revolution, he says,
"Almost everywhere . . . intellectual persons did not comprehend what was happening. Certainly the writers didn't. Plenty
of them shuddered away, as though the right course for a man
of feeling was to contract out; some, like Ruskin and William
Morris and Thoreau and Emerson and Lawrence, tried various
kinds of fancies, which were not much in effect more than
screams of horror. It is hard to think of a writer of high class

who really stretched his imaginative sympathy, who could see at once the hideous back-streets, the smoking chimneys, the internal price—and also the prospects of life that were opening out for the poor. . . ."

Nothing could be further from the truth. No great English writer of the 19th century, once he had become aware of the Industrial Revolution, ever contracted out. This is not the place to rehearse the miseries that were acquiesced in by those who comforted the world and their own consciences with the thought of "the prospects of life that were opening out for the poor." It is enough to say that there were miseries in plenty, of a brutal and horrifying kind, by no means adequately suggested by phrases like "the hideous back-streets, the smoking chimneys, the internal price." (Auschwitz, since it has been mentioned, may be thought of as the development of the conditions of the factories and mines of the earlier Industrial Revolution.) If the writers "shuddered away," it was not in maidenly disgust with machines and soot; if they uttered "screams of horror," it was out of moral outrage at what man had made of man—and of women and little children. Their emotions were no different from those expressed by Karl Marx in his chapter on the Working Day, nor from those expressed in Blue Books by the factory inspectors, those remarkable men of the middle class whom Marx, in a moving passage of *Capital*, praises and wonders at for their transcendence of their class feelings.

I have mentioned Matthew Arnold among those writers who made the old conditions of the Industrial Revolution ever less possible. Like many of his colleagues in this undertaking, he did entertain "fancies"—they all found modern life ugly and fatiguing and in some way false, and they set store by certain qualities which are no doubt traditional to the point of being archaic.[3] But Arnold's peculiar distinction as a literary critic is founded on the strong sensitivity of his response to the modern situation. He uniquely understood what Hegel had told the world, that the French Revolution marked an absolute change

[3] Emerson doesn't deserve Sir Charles's scorn on this point. His advice to the American scholar was that he should respond positively to the actual and the modern, and he was inclined to take an almost too unreserved pleasure in new forms of human energy and ingenuity. As for Thoreau, his quarrel was not with factories but with farms—and families.

in the condition of man. For the first time in history, Hegel said, Reason—or Idea, or Theory, or Creative Imagination—had become decisive in human destiny. Arnold's argument in "Literature and Science" was the affirmation of the French Revolution; he was speaking on behalf of the illumination and refinement of that Reason by which man might shape the conditions of his own existence. This is the whole purport of his famous statement, "Literature is the criticism of life."

That saying used to have a rough time of it, perhaps because people found the word criticism narrow and dour and wished to believe that life was worthier of being celebrated than criticized. But less and less, I think, will anyone find the ground on which to quarrel with it. Whatever else we also take literature to be, it must always, for us now, be the criticism of life.

But it would seem to be precisely the critical function of literature that troubles Sir Charles. And perhaps that is why, despite all that he says about the need to educate ourselves, he does not make a single substantive proposal about education.

If we undertake to say what the purpose of modern education is, our answer will surely be suggested by Arnold's phrase, together with the one by which he defined the particular function of criticism: "to see the object as in itself it really is." Whenever we undertake to pass judgment on an educational enterprise, the import of these two phrases serves as our criterion: we ask that education supply the means for a criticism of life and teach the student to try to see the object as in itself it really is. Yet when Sir Charles speaks of the need to break the "existing pattern" and to go on to a right education, he does not touch upon any such standard of judgment. Although he would seem to be the likeliest person in the world to speak intelligently about the instruction in science of students who do not intend to be scientists, actually he says nothing more on the subject than that ignorance of the Second Law of Thermodynamics is equivalent to ignorance of Shakespeare, or that the Yang-Lee experiment at Columbia should have been a topic of general conversation at college High Tables.

Nor does he propose anything for the education of the scientist, except, of course, science. He does say that scientists need to be "trained not only in scientific but in human terms," but he does not say how. Scientists—but eventually one begins to wonder if they are really scientists and not advanced technologists and engineers—are to play a decisive part in the affairs of mankind, but nowhere does Sir Charles suggest that, if this is so, they will face difficulties and perplexities and that their education should include the study of books—they need not be "literary," they need not be "traditional": they might be contemporary works of history, sociology, anthropology, psychology, philosophy—which would raise the difficult questions and propose the tragic complexity of the human condition, which would suggest that it is not always easy to see the object as in itself it really is.

Well, it isn't beyond belief that a professional corps of high intellectual quality, especially if it is charged with great responsibility, should learn to ask its own questions and go on to make its own ethos, perhaps a very good one. But Sir Charles would seem to be asking for more than the right of scientists to go their own way. What he seems to require for scientists is the right to go their own way *with no questions asked.* The culture of literature, having done its worst, must now be supplanted and is not ever to play the part of a loyal opposition. How else are we to understand Sir Charles's contempt for the irresponsibility of the literary mind, his curious representation of the literary culture as having the management of the Western world, that is to say, as being answerable for all the anomalies, stupidities, and crimes of the Western world, for having made the "existing pattern" which must now be broken if the West is to survive or at least not suffer steep decline? It is manifest that the literary culture has lost the right to ask questions.

No one could possibly suppose of Charles Snow that he is a man who wants to curtail the rights of free criticism. The line which he takes in *The Two Cultures* is so far from the actuality of his temperament in this respect that we can only suppose that he doesn't mean it, not in all the extravagance of its literalness. Or we suppose that he means it at the behest of some large preoccupation of whose goodness he is so entirely convinced that he will seek to affirm it even in ways that would take him aback if the preoccupation were not in control of his thought. And this, I think, is the case. I believe that the position of *The Two Cultures* is to be explained by Sir Charles's preoccupation—it has become almost the best-known thing about him—with a good and necessary aim, with the assuring of peace, which is to say, with the compounding of the differences between the West and the Soviet Union. It is an aim which, in itself, can of course only do Sir Charles credit, yet it would seem to have implicit in it a strange desperate method of implementing itself.

For the real message of *The Two Cultures* is that an understanding between the West and the Soviet Union could be achieved by the culture of scientists, which reaches over factitious national and ideological differences. The field of agreement would be the scientists' common perception of the need for coming together to put the possibilities of the scientific revolution at the disposal of the disadvantaged of all nations. The bond between scientists, Sir Charles has told us, is virtually biological: they all have the future in their bones. Science brings men together in despite of all barriers—speaking of the way in which the very wide differences in the class origins of English scientists were overcome to make the scientific culture of England (and seeming to imply that this is a unique grace of scientists, that English men of letters never had differences of class to overcome), Sir Charles says, "Without thinking about it, they respond alike. That is what a culture means." And in the same way, "without thinking about it," the scientists of the West and the scientists of the Soviet Union may be expected to "respond alike." And, since "that is what a culture means," they will have joined together in an entity which will do what governments have not done, the work of relieving the misery of the world. But in the degree to which science naturally unites men, literature separates them, and the scientists of the world cannot form this beneficent entity until we of the West break the existing pattern of our traditional culture, the literary culture, which is self-regarding in its complacent acceptance of tragedy, which is not only indifferent to human suffering but willing to inflict it, which asks rude and impertinent questions about the present and even about the future.

It is a point of view that must, I suppose, in desperate days, have a show of reason. In desperate days, it always seems wise to throw something or someone overboard, preferably Jonah or Arion, the prophet or the poet. Mr. G. S. Fraser, for example, seems to understand what Sir Charles wants, and he is rather willing to go along with him, rather open to the idea that the achievement of peace may require some adverse judgment on literature. "It does not matter," he says, "whether we save the real Cambridge within the actual Cambridge . . . ; what we want to save is our actual human world with all the spots on it. This will not be done by teaching English at universities; men like Snow, at home both in Russia and America, and in a simple blunt way trying to teach these two blunt simple giants to understand each other may in the end prove greater benefactors than Dr. Leavis."

No, the world will not be saved by teaching English at universities, nor, indeed, by any other literary activity. It is very hard to say what will save the world, and pretty surely it is no one single thing. But we can be perfectly certain that the world will not be saved by denying the actualities of the world. Among these actualities politics is one. And it can be said of *The Two Cultures* that it communicates the strongest possible wish that we should forget about politics. It mentions national politics once, speaking of it as the clog upon the activity of scientists, as the impeding circumstance in which they must work. But the point is not developed and the lecture has the effect of suggesting that the issue is not between the abilities and good intentions of scientists and the inertia or bad will of governments; the issue is represented as being between the good culture of science and the bad culture of literature.

In this denial of the actuality of politics, Sir Charles is at one with the temper of intellectuals today—we all want politics not to exist, we all want that statement of Hegel's to be absolutely and immediately true, we dream of Reason taking over the whole management of the world, and soon. No doubt a beneficent eventuality, but our impatience for it is dangerous if it leads us to deny the actuality of politics in the present. While we discuss, at Sir Charles's instance, the relative merits of scientific Philosopher Kings as against literary Philosopher

Kings, politics goes on living its own autonomous life, of which
one aspect is its massive resistance to Reason. What is gained
by describing the resistance to Reason as other than it is, by
thinking in the specious terms of two opposing "cultures"?

But of course the fact is that politics is not finally autonomous. It may be so massively resistant to Reason that we are
led to think of its resistance as absolute—in bad times we conceive politics to be nothing but power. Yet it cannot be said—
at least not so long as politics relies in any degree upon ideology
—that politics is never susceptible to such Reason as is expressed
in opinion, only that it is less susceptible in some nations and
at some times than in other nations and at other times. And
nowhere and at no time is politics exempt from moral judgment,
whether or not that judgment is effectual. But if we make believe, as *The Two Cultures* does, that politics does not exist at
all, then it cannot be the object of moral judgment. And if we
deny all authority to literature, as *The Two Cultures* does, going
so far as to say that the great traditional agency of moral awareness is itself immoral, then the very activity of moral judgment
is impugned, except for that single instance of it which asserts
the rightness of bringing the benefits of science to the disadvantaged of the world. In short, Sir Charles, seeking to advance
the cause of understanding between the West and the Soviet
Union, would seem to be saying that this understanding will
come if we conceive both that politics cannot be judged (because it does not really exist) and that it should not be judged
(because the traditional agency of judgment is irresponsible).

III

I judge *The Two Cultures* to be a book which is mistaken
in a very large way indeed. And I find the failure of Dr. Leavis's
criticism of it to consist in his addressing himself not to the
full extent of its error but to extraneous matters. From reading
the Richmond Lecture one gains the impression that the substance of the Rede Lecture is extremely offensive to Dr. Leavis,
that all his sensibilities are outraged by it: we conclude that
Sir Charles wants something which is very different from what
Dr. Leavis wants, and that Dr. Leavis thinks that what Sir
Charles wants is crude and vulgar. But we can scarcely suppose

from Dr. Leavis's response that what Sir Charles says has a very wide reference—for all we can tell, he might have been proposing a change in the university curriculum which Dr. Leavis is repelling with the violence and disgust that are no doubt often felt though not expressed at meetings of curriculum committees. For Dr. Leavis, who has always attached great importance to educational matters, the proposed change is certainly important beyond the university. He understands it both as likely to have a bad effect on the national culture and as being the expression of something already bad in the national culture. But this, we suppose, he would feel about any change in the curriculum.

In short, Dr. Leavis, in dealing with the Rede Lecture, has not seen the object as in itself it really is, just as Sir Charles, in dealing with the culture of literature in its relation to politics, has not seen the object as in itself it really is.

An example of the inadequacy of Dr. Leavis's criticism of *The Two Cultures* is his response to what Sir Charles says, in concert with the distinguished scientist, about the political posture of the great writers of the modern period. That statement, if we stop short of its mention of Auschwitz—which makes a most important modification—certainly does have a color of truth. It is one of the cultural curiosities of the first three decades of the 20th century that, while the educated people, the readers of books, tended to become ever more liberal and radical in their thought, there is no literary figure of the very first rank (although many of the next rank) who, in his work, makes use of or gives credence to liberal or radical ideas. I remarked on this circumstance in an essay of 1946. "Our educated class," I said, "has a ready if mild suspiciousness of the profit motive, a belief in progress, science, social legislation, planning, and international cooperation, perhaps especially where Russia is in question. These beliefs do great credit to those who hold them. Yet it is a comment, if not on our beliefs then on our way of holding them, that not a single first-rate writer has emerged to deal with these ideas, and the emotions that are consonant with them, in a great literary way. . . . If we name those writers who, by the general consent of the most serious criticism, by consent too of the very class of educated people of which we speak, are thought of as the monumental figures of our time, we see that to these writers the liberal ideology has been at best a matter of indifference. Proust, Joyce, Lawrence, Yeats, Mann [as novelist], Kafka, Rilke, Gide [also as novelist] —all of them have their own love of justice and the good life, but in not one of them does it take the form of a love of the ideas and emotions which liberal democracy, as known by our educated class, has declared respectable." To which it can be added that some great writers have in their work given credence or utterance to conservative and even reactionary ideas, and that some in their personal lives maintained a settled indifference to all political issues, or a disdain of them. No reader is likely to derive political light either from the works or the table-talk of a modern literary genius, and some readers (of weak mind) might even be led into bad political ways.

If these writers are to be brought to the bar of judgment, any-one who speaks as their advocate is not, as Sir Charles says, defending the indefensible. The advocacy can be conducted in honest and simple ways. It is not one of these ways to say that literature is by its nature or by definition innocent—it is power-ful enough for us to suppose that it has the possibility of doing harm. But the ideational influence of literature is by no means always as direct as, for polemical purposes, people sometimes say it is. As against the dismay of Sir Charles and the distin-guished scientist at the reactionary tendencies of modern literary geniuses, there is the fact—a bald one—that the English poets who learned their trade from Yeats and Eliot, or even from Pound, have notably had no sympathy with the social ideas and attitudes of their poetical masters.

Every university teacher of literature will have observed the circumstance that young people who are of radical social and political opinion are virtually never troubled by the opposed views or the settled indifference of the great modern writers. This is not because the young exempt the writer from dealing with the serious problems of living, or because they see him through a mere aesthetic haze. It is because they know—and quite without instruction—that, in D. H. Lawrence's words, they are to trust the tale and not the teller of the tale. They perceive that the tale is always on the side of their own gener-ous impulses. They know that, if the future is in the bones of anyone, it is in the bones of the literary genius, and exactly because the present is in his bones, exactly because the past is in his bones. They know that if a work of literature has any true artistic existence, it has value as a criticism of life; in whatever complex way it has chosen to speak, it is making a declaration about the qualities that life should have, about the qualities life does not have but should have. They feel, I think, that it is simply not possible for a work of literature that comes within the borders of greatness *not* to ask for more energy and fineness of life, and, by its own communication of awareness, bring these qualities into being. And if, in their experience of such a work, they happen upon an expression of contempt for some idea which they have connected with political virtue, they are not slow to understand that it is not the idea in its ideal form that is being despised, but the idea as it passes current in specious form, among certain and particular persons. I have yet to meet the student committed to an altruistic politics who is alienated from Stephen Daedalus by that young man's disgust with political idealism, just as I have yet to meet the student from the most disadvantaged background who feels debarred from what Yeats can give him by the poet's slurs upon shopkeepers or by anything else in his inexhaustible fund of snobbery.

If ever a man was qualified to state the case for literature, and far more persuasively than I have done, it is Dr. Leavis. His career as a critic and a teacher has been devoted exactly to the exposition of the idea that literature presents to us "the possibilities of life," the qualities of energy and fineness that life might have. And it is, of course, the intention of the Richmond Lecture to say just this in answer to Sir Charles's indictment. Yet something checks Dr. Leavis. When it is a question of the defense, not of literature in general, but of modern literature, he puts into countervailing evidence nothing more than a passage in which Lawrence says something, in a wry and grudging way, on behalf of social equality. This does not meet the charge; against it Sir Charles might cite a dozen instances in which Lawrence utters what Sir Charles—and perhaps even Dr. Leavis himself—would consider "the most imbecile expressions of anti-social feeling."

There is only one feasible approach to the anti-social utterances of many modern writers, and that is to consider whether their expressions of anti-social feeling are nothing but imbecile. It is the fact, like it or not, that a characteristic cultural enterprise of our time has been the questioning of society itself, not its particular forms and aspects but its very essence. To this extreme point has the criticism of life extended itself. Of the ways of dealing with this phenomenon, that of horror and dismay, such as Sir Charles's, is perhaps the least useful. Far better, it seems to me, is the effort to understand what this passionate hostility to society implies, to ask whether it is a symptom, sufficiently gross, of the decline of the West, or whether it is not perhaps an act of critical energy on the part of the West, an act of critical energy on the part of society itself—the effort of society to identify in itself that which is but speciously good, the effort to understand afresh the nature of the life it is designed to foster. I would not anticipate the answer, but these questions make, I am sure, the right way to come at the phenomenon.

It is not the way that Dr. Leavis comes at the phenomenon, despite his saying that the university study of literature must take its stand on the "intellectual-cultural frontier." Of the two D. H. Lawrences, the one who descended from the social-minded 19th century and who did, in some sort, affirm the social idea, and the other, for whom the condition of salvation was the total negation of society, Dr. Leavis can be comfortable only with the former. For the fact is that his commitment to the intellectual-cultural frontier is sincere but chiefly theoretical; he has, as is well known, sympathy with very few modern writers, and he therefore cannot in good grace come to their defense against Sir Charles's characterization of them.

Mr. Walter Allen, writing in the *New York Times Book Review*, has accurately remarked on "the common areas of agreement" between Dr. Leavis and Sir Charles. "One would expect . . . that Snow would be sympathetic to Leavis's emphasis on the all-importance of the moral center of literature," Mr. Allen says. "Both have attacked experiment in literature.

Neither of them, to put it into crude shorthand, are Flaubert-and-Joyce men." The similarities go further. In point of social background the two men are not much apart, at least to the untutored American eye. Both spring from the provincial middle class in one or another of its strata, and whatever differences there may have been in the material advantages that were available or lacking to one or the other, neither was reared in the assumption of easy privilege. From these origins they derived, we may imagine, their strong sense of quotidian actuality and a respect for those who discharge the duties it imposes, and a high regard for the domestic affections, a quick dislike of the frivolous and merely elegant. Neither, as I have suggested, has any least responsiveness to the tendencies of modern thought or literature which are existential or subversive. A lively young person of advanced tastes would surely say that if ever two men were committed to England, Home, and Duty, they are Leavis and Snow—he would say that in this they are as alike as two squares.

There is one other regard, an especially significant one, in which they are similar. This is their feeling about social class. One of the chief interests of Sir Charles's novels is their explicitness about class as a determinative of the personal life, and in this respect *The Two Cultures* is quite as overt as the novels—its scientists make a new class by virtue of their alienation from the old class attitudes, and Sir Charles's identification of literary men with the traditional culture which supposedly manages the Western world implies that they are in effect the representatives of an aristocratic ruling class, decadent but still powerful. The work of Dr. Leavis is no less suffused by the idea of social class, even though its preoccupation with the subject is far less explicit. To my recollection, Dr. Leavis does not make use of any of the words which denote the distinctions of English society—he does not refer to an aristocracy, a gentry, an upper-middle or lower-middle or working class. For him a class defines itself by its idea of itself—that is, by its tastes and style. Class is for him a cultural entity. And when he conceives of class power, as he often does, it is not economic or political power but, rather, cultural power that he thinks of. It is true that cultural power presents itself to his mind as being in some way suggestive of class power, but the actualities of power or influence are for him always secondary to the culture from which they arose or to which they give rise.

And indeed, no less than Sir Charles, Dr. Leavis is committed to the creation of a new class. This, we might even say, is the whole motive of his work. The social situation he would seem to assume is one in which there is a fair amount of mobility which is yet controlled and limited by the tendency of the mobile people to allow themselves to be absorbed into one of the traditional classes. As against the attraction exerted by a quasi-aristocratic, metropolitan upper-middle class, Dr. Leavis has taken it to be his function to organize the mobile people, those of them who are gifted and conscious, into a new social class formed on the basis of its serious understanding of and response to literature, chiefly English literature. In this undertaking he has by no means been wholly unsuccessful. One has the impression that many of the students he has trained think of themselves, as they take up their posts in secondary schools and universities, as constituting at least a social cadre.

The only other time I wrote about Dr. Leavis I remarked that the Cromwellian Revolution had never really come to an end in England and that Dr. Leavis was one of the chief colonels of the Roundhead party. His ideal readers are people who "are seriously interested in literature," and it is on their behalf that he wages war againts a cultural-social class which, when it concerns itself with literature, avows its preference for the qualities of grace, lightness, and irony, and deprecates an overt sincerity and seriousness. "To a polished nation," said Gibbon, "poetry is an amusement of the fancy, not a passion of the soul," and all through his career it is against everything that Gibbon means by a polished nation and might mean by a polished class that Dr. Leavis has set his face. Bloomsbury has been his characteristic antagonist. But now, in Charles Snow, he confronts an opponent who is as Roundhead as himself, and as earnest and *intentional*.

To this confrontation Dr. Leavis is not adequate. It is not an adequate response to the massive intention of *The Two*

Cultures for Dr. Leavis to meet Sir Charles's cultural preferences with his own preferences; or to seek to discredit Sir Charles's ideas chiefly by making them out to be vulgar ideas or outmoded (Wellsian) ideas; or to offer, as against Sir Charles's vision of a future made happier by science, the charms of primitive peoples "with their marvellous arts and skills and vital intelligence." I do not mean to say that Dr. Leavis does not know where Sir Charles goes wrong in the details of his argument—he is as clear as we expect him to be in rebuking that quite massive blunder about the Victorian writers. Nor, certainly, do I mean that Dr. Leavis does not know what the great fundamental mistake of Sir Charles's position is—he does, and he can be eloquent in asserting against a simplistic confidence in a scientific "future" the need of mankind, in the face of a rapid advance of science and technology, "to be in full intelligent possession of its full humanity (and 'possession' here means, not confident ownership of that which belongs to *us*—our property, but a basic living deference towards that to which, opening as it does into the unknown and itself immeasurable, we know we belong)." But such moments of largeness do not save the Richmond Lecture from its general aspect of dealing with an issue that is essentially parochial. For example, of the almost limitless political implications of Sir Charles's position it gives no evidence of awareness. And if we undertake to find a reason for the inadequacy of Dr. Leavis's response, we will find, I think, that it is the same as the reason which accounts for Sir Charles having been in the first place so wholly mistaken in what he says—both men set too much store by the idea of *culture* as a category of thought.

The concept of culture is an idea of great attractiveness and undoubted usefulness. We may say that it begins in the assumption that all human expressions or artifacts are indicative of some considerable tendencies in the life of social groups or sub-groups, and that what is indicative is also causative—all cultural facts have their consequences. To think in cultural terms is to consider human expressions not only in their overt existence and avowed intention, but in, as it were, their secret life, taking cognizance of the desires and impulses which lie behind the open formulation. In the judgments which we make when we think in the category of culture we rely to a very large extent upon the style in which an expression is made, believing that style will indicate, or betray, what is not intended to be expressed. The aesthetic mode is integral to the idea of culture, and our judgments of social groups are likely to be made chiefly on an aesthetic basis—we like or do not like what we call their life-styles, and even when we judge moralities, the criterion by which we choose between two moralities of, say, equal strictness or equal laxness is likely to be an aesthetic one.

The concept of culture affords to those who use it a sense of the liberation of their thought, for they deal less with abstractions and mere objects, more with the momentous actualities of human feelings as these shape and condition the human community, as they make and as they indicate the quality of man's existence. Not the least of the attractions of the cultural mode of thought are the passions which attend it —because it assumes that all things are causative or indicative of the whole of the cultural life, it proposes to us those intensities of moralized feeling which seem appropriate to our sense that all that is good in life is at stake in every cultural action. An instance of mediocrity or failure in art or thought is not only what it is but also a sin, deserving to be treated as such. These passions are vivifying; they have the semblance of heroism.

And if we undertake to say what were the circumstances that made the cultural mode of thought as available and as authoritative as it now is, we must refer to Marx, and to Freud, and to the general movement of existentialism, to all that the tendencies of modernity imply of the sense of contingency in life, from which we learn that the one thing that can be disputed, and that is worth disputing, is preference or taste. The Rede Lecture and the Richmond Lecture exemplify the use to which the idea of culture can be put in shaking the old certainties of class, in contriving new social groups on the basis of taste. All this does indeed give the cultural mode of thought a very considerable authority. Yet sometimes we may wonder if it is wholly an accident that so strong an impulse to base our sense of life, and our conduct of the intellectual life, chiefly upon the confrontations of taste should have developed in an age dominated by advertising, the wonderful and terrible art which teaches us that we define ourselves and realize our true being by choosing the right style. In our more depressed moments we might be led to ask whether there is a real difference between being The Person Who defines himself by his commitment to one or another idea of morality, politics, literature, or city-planning, and being The Person Who defines himself by wearing trousers without pleats.

We can, I suppose, no more escape from the cultural mode of thought than we can escape from culture itself. Yet perhaps we must learn to cast a somewhat colder eye upon it for the sake of whatever regard we have for the intellectual life, for the possibility of rational discourse. Sir Charles envisages a new and very powerful social class on the basis of a life-style which he imputes to a certain profession in contrast with the life-style he imputes to another profession, and he goes on from there to deny both the reality of politics and the possibility of its being judged by moral standards. Dr. Leavis answers him with a passion of personal scorn which obscures the greater part of the issue and offers in contradiction truth indeed but truth so hampered and hidden by the defenses of Dr. Leavis's own choice in life-styles that it looks not much different from a prejudice. And the *Spectator* correspondents exercise their taste in life-styles and take appropriate sides. It is at such a moment that our dispirited minds yearn to find comfort and courage in the idea of Mind, that faculty whose ancient potency our commitment to the idea of culture denies. To us today, Mind must inevitably seem but a poor gray thing, for it always sought to detach itself from the passions (but not from the emotions, Spinoza said, and explained the difference) and from the conditions of time and place. Yet it is salutary for us to contemplate it, whatever its grayness, because of the bright belief that was once attached to it, that it was the faculty which belonged not to professions, or to social classes, or to cultural groups, but to Man, and that it was possible for men, and becoming to them, to learn its proper use, for it was the means by which they could communicate with each other.

It was on this belief that science based its early existence, and it gave to the men who held it a character which is worth remarking. Sir Charles mentions Faraday among those scientists who over-rode the limitations of social class to form the "scientific culture" of England. This is true only so far as it can be made consonant with the fact that Faraday could not have imagined the idea of a "scientific culture" and would have been wholly repelled by it. It is told of Faraday that he refused to be called a *physicist*; he very much disliked the new name as being too special and particular and insisted on the old one, *philosopher*, in all its spacious generality: we may suppose that this was his way of saying that he had not over-ridden the limiting conditions of class only to submit to the limitations of profession. The idea of Mind which had taught the bookbinder's apprentice to embark on his heroic enterprise of self-instruction also taught the great scientist to place himself beyond the specialness of interest which groups prescribe for their members. Every personal episode in Tyndall's classic account of his master, *Faraday as a Researcher*, makes it plain that Faraday undertook to be, in the beautiful lost sense of the word, a *disinterested* man. From his belief in Mind, he derived the certitude that he had his true being not as a member of this or that profession or class, but as—in the words of a poet of his time— "a man speaking to men."

No one now needs to be reminded of what may befall the idea of Mind in the way of excess and distortion. The literature of the 19th century never wearied of telling us just this, of decrying the fatigue and desiccation of spirit which result from an allegiance to Mind that excludes impulse and will, and desire and preference. It was, surely, a liberation to be made aware of this, and then to go on to take serious account of those particularities of impulse and will, of desire and preference, which differentiate individuals and groups—to employ what I have called the cultural mode of thought. We take it for granted that this, like any other mode of thought, has its peculiar dangers, but there is cause for surprise and regret that it should be Sir Charles Snow and Dr. Leavis who have jointly demonstrated how far the cultural mode of thought can go in excess and distortion.

CHARLES DARWIN, THE ANAESTHETIC MAN

Donald Fleming

Here are three voices from Victorian England.

"What do I know of tastes and fancies? What escape have I had from problems that could be demonstrated, and realities that could be grasped? If I had been stone blind; if I had groped my way by my sense of touch, and had been free, while I knew the shapes and surfaces of things, to exercise my fancy somewhat, in regard to them; I should have been a million times wiser, happier, more loving, more contented, more innocent and human in all good respects, than I am with the eyes I have."—"I never knew you were unhappy."—"I always knew it."

I became persuaded, that my love of mankind, and of excellence for its own sake, had worn itself out. For I now saw, what I had always before received with incredulity—that the habit of analysis has a tendency to wear away the feelings. I was left stranded at the commencement of my voyage, with a well-equipped ship and a rudder, but no sail. The fountains of vanity and ambition seemed to have dried up within me, as completely as those of benevolence. I frequently asked myself if I could go on living.

I have tried lately to read Shakespeare, and found it so intolerably dull that it nauseated me. I have also almost lost my taste for pictures or music. I am glad you were at the 'Messiah,' but I dare say I should find my soul too dried up to appreciate it; and then I should feel very flat, for it is a horrid bore to feel as I constantly do, that I am a withered leaf for every subject except Science. The loss of these tastes is a loss of happiness. My mind seems to have become a kind of machine for grinding general laws out of large collections of facts. It sometimes makes me hate Science.

The first speaker is Louisa in Dickens' *Hard Times* of 1854.[1]

From *Victorian Studies*, IV (March, 1961), 219–236. Reprinted by permission of Donald Fleming and *Victorian Studies*.

[1] Conflated and abbreviated from Bk. I, ch. xv, and Bk. II, ch. xii. The most stimulating analysis of *Hard Times*, by which I have been greatly influenced, is by F. R. Leavis in *The Great Tradition* (London, 1948).

The second is John Stuart Mill in his *Autobiography* of 1873, describing a crisis that he passed through in the winter of 1826–27.[2] The third is Charles Darwin in a letter of 1868 and his autobiography of 1876.[3] Most historians would say that Dickens is validated by Mill and Darwin. One might argue instead that recollections of the inner life have to be validated by art in their representative historical character. One thing is certain, when the same theme reverberates upon itself from life to art and back again, the historian had better pay attention.

The common predicament of the fictional Louisa and the real Mill and Darwin may be described as the dissociation of knowledge and sensibility; fact and affect. They know but cannot feel and are afraid to feel and fearful of not feeling—joyless, parched, and worn-out. I am tired, says the young Louisa, "I have been tired a long time" (Bk. I, ch. iii). Louisa's state of exhaustion is the product of her father Thomas Gradgrind's fact-system of education. "Facts alone are wanted in life. Plant nothing else, and root out everything else" (Bk. I, ch. i). Over against the Gradgrinds of Coketown Dickens put the orphan circus-girl Sissy Jupe, lamentably brought up on the "destructive nonsense" of *A Thousand and One Nights* and other fairy tales and predictably unable to see why she cannot have flowers on carpets for the fancy of it, where they would get crushed if real and if not real have no business being there. " 'They wouldn't crush or wither, if you please, Sir. They would be pictures of what was very pretty and pleasant, and I would fancy—' 'Ay, ay, ay. But you musn't fancy' " (Bk. I, ch. ii). Sissy is an emblem of the circus acrobats from whom she came, with their emotional abundance and immediacy of feeling and their power of taking up easy attitudes and dispensing ease to others—artists who stacked themselves up in pyramids to lift the people of Coketown clean out of the Flood of Facts. The Gradgrinds are Utilitarians, Political Ecnomists, Statisticians; in Dickens's terrible figure, dustmen raising clouds of dust to stifle feeling. The circus people are human beings fulfilling the human con-

[2] Conflated, abbreviated, and rearranged from *Autobiography*, ed. John J. Coss (New York, 1924), pp. 96–99.

[3] Conflated, abbreviated, and rearranged from Francis Darwin, ed., *The Life and Letters of Charles Darwin* (London, 1887), III, 92; and *The Autobiography of Charles Darwin, 1809–1882*, ed. Nora Barlow (London, 1958), pp. 138–139.

dition. In the end only Sissy Jupe can nurse Louisa into humanness.

John Stuart Mill was dusty from the cradle. He was a product of the same philosophy of education that Dickens satirized in *Hard Times*, Benthamite Utilitarianism (*Autobiography*, pp. 27–36). James Mill, the father, was a man of more spacious views than Thomas Gradgrind; and more than this, he had a not merely ideal but felt aversion from pain and suffering. Religion to him was intolerable as postulating an omnipotent and benevolent god as the ground of such evil. He was, his son thought, a man of deep feelings who could not imagine they would be in short supply with anybody else. Education was needed as a bridle upon them and could never lack for a mount to rein in. For this reason it did not occur to him to make good in his education of his son the characteristic Benthamite undervaluation of poetry and imagination. Bentham himself had said, notoriously, that "all poetry is misrepresentation," to which the younger Mill enters the odd demurrer that the old man did not really mean that *poetry* was misrepresentation but merely anything at all that was "more oratorical in its character than a sum in arithmetic" (*Autobiography*, p. 78). Which clears that up. John Stuart Mill as a boy actually did read some poetry—including Pope's *Essay on Man*—but he was like his preceptors in not being able to connect this with the real business of life, to beat abuses over the head with facts. So the boy grew up, speculatively benevolent to all mankind but mainly speculative, and headed straight for deadness of heart.

When the doldrums had come and withered him up and he had no wind to puff his sails, he tried to find help in Byron, but that was no good—"Harold and Manfred had the same burden on them which I had" (*Autobiography*, p. 103). The true medicine was Wordsworth, who dealt in "states of feeling, and of thought coloured by feeling, under the excitement of beauty" —"they seemed to be the very culture of the feelings, which I was in quest of" (*Autobiography*, p. 104). The lesson that Wordsworth drove home to Mill about the necessity of poetry and art as "instruments of human culture," the best means to cultivation of the "passive susceptibilities," he tried to pass on in turn to other Utilitarians, most notably the young Radical politician J. A. Roebuck, already a lover of music, painting, and

Byronic poetry, but like the rest unable to see that these things
had any value as "aids in the formation of character" (*Autobiography*, pp. 105–107). Cultivation of the feelings through
the imagination, Roebuck told him, was "only cultivating illu-
sions." Mill thought that underneath, Roebuck was like his
own father, endowed with "quick and strong sensibilities" but
"more susceptible to the painful sympathies than to the pleasur-
able" and seeking to deaden his feelings rather than stir them
up. If what John Stuart Mill had to say in praise of poetry could
give offense to Utilitarians, his mature view on the role of music
would have been more alarming still: it surpassed all other arts
in "exciting enthusiasm; in winding up to a high pitch those
feelings of an elevated kind which are already in the character,
but to which this excitement gives a glow and a fervour, which,
though transitory at its utmost height, is precious for sustaining
them at other times" (*Autobiography*, p. 101). This exaltation
of irresponsible excitement was like ushering an obscene force
out of nightmares into the hard clear daytime of Benthamism—
a fund of free-floating emotional energy, unexpended and
unspoken-for, mere dangerous potentiality declining to be
trussed up and handed over to any determinate end. The cure
that Wordsworth had commenced, Mill's only love Helen Taylor completed—a Shelley among women in feeling, he said, a
veritable Mill in liberation from superstition, as he might have
added, and one integral being, who gave proof that Mill to be a
whole man would not have to give up his father's warfare upon
religion and all other forms of acquiescence in the evil of the
world.

I

Louisa Gradgrind and John Stuart Mill after many vain attempts passed through the door of feeling into life. Charles
Darwin traced the opposite course from a carefree youth to a
desiccated old age when many doors that gave upon the world
of art and feeling had slammed upon him (Darwin, *Autobiography*). From the time of his mother's death when he was only
eight, the young Darwin had his whole being in the immense
shadow of his father—340 pounds the last time they dared to
weigh him, with an almost Johnsonian force of personality to
match—but the latter never tried to mold him to order or

sought to impose his own conviction that religious belief was unworthy of an intelligent man. Darwin as a young man responded to this permissive environment by displaying a catholic enthusiasm for life. His chief pleasure, indeed passion, was hunting, and he got plenty of it in, the anthem in King's Chapel made him shiver with delight, he loved Raphael and Sebastian del Piombo, Handel's *Messiah* and Maria Malibran, Shakespeare and Milton, Wordsworth and Coleridge, and fine scenery into the bargin. He was bored by long stretches of his education but was always permitted to move on to something else and some other prospective career. He began by preparing to be a physician like his father, but between the tedium of the lectures and the horror of operations before chloroform, of which the memory hounded him "for many a long year," he decided to call it a bad job, and Dr. Darwin acquiesced. He himself avoided being present at surgery and could not bear the sight of blood. Their next idea was the clergy, which would never have been the father's choice for himself but anything sooner than an idle sporting life, and the son thought it would be all right if he got a country living with a continual round of hunting and natural history, punctuated by a few sermons. Dogma was no problem. All 39 Articles went down smoothly. It never struck him at the time, he later wrote, "how illogical it was to say that I believed in what I could not understand and what is in fact unintelligible." That was later. On the great voyage of the *Beagle,* Darwin passed among his shipmates for naïvely religious and given to crediting the letter of the Bible in a way that was already old-fashioned. If this was mere habit, he several times in the course of the expedition felt an experiential influx of "the sublime"—"the higher feelings of wonder, admiration, and devotion," which bore irresistible testimony to God and the immortality of the soul (*Autobiography*, p. 91). Once he stood upon the summit of the Andes and surveyed the magnificent prospect all around and felt "as if his nerves had become fiddlestrings, and had all taken to rapidly vibrating" (*Life and Letters*, III, 54). But he felt "most sublime" of all in the rainforests of Brazil, corresponding to the jungle red in tooth and claw of the homekeeping Tennyson but to Darwin on the spot a source of incommunicable delight, more gorgeous even than the landscapes of Claude Lorrain—his own comparison. Under the spell of the sublime Darwin did not see the jungle as an arena of combat to be shunned by sensitive men but as an occasion for rejoicing and deep assent to the universe. The thing that made him cringe was the uneven contest between slaves and their masters. "The remembrance," his son says, "of screams, or other sounds heard in Brazil, where he was powerless to interfere with what he believed to be the torture of a slave, haunted him for years, especially at night" (*Life and Letters*, III, 200). With these deep echoes resounding through his spirit and the queer fauna of oceanic islands teasing his brain, Darwin returned to England in 1836. In the course of the next two years he thought a good deal about religion, found that he could less and less imagine any evidence that would persuade him of the truth of Christianity, and came to think that even if true it was a "damnable doctrine" for condemning to eternal punishment unbelievers like his father and elder brother (*Autobiography*, pp. 86–87). In theory, and more or less in practice, this left open the question whether Darwin might still be able to salvage some kind of theism from the ruins of his now exploded orthodoxy. He had already gone far enough in unconventionality to make his father advise him to keep any future wife in the dark.

It was pertinent advice. In the same period when he began to find revealed religion wanting, Darwin was also canvassing in the abstract whether to get married or not. One credit item for getting married ran that a wife would be something to play with and better than a dog anyhow. Marriage it was, but marriage to a commonplace woman, deeply though not illiberally religious; no Helen Taylor to energize and set him free and add her strength to his own. It is clear that in the midst of her tender care for him, Emma Darwin was not above administering the most loving possible pinpricks on the subject of religion; for Darwin did not take his father's advice but told her everything. One gets the impression that she was always checking herself bravely on the verge of lamenting her husband's unregenerate state and professing not quite to believe that he really wasn't religious and she of course was just a poor muddleheaded little woman and he musn't mind her but had he thought of *this* argument for religion (*Autobiography*, pp. 235–238). He says, in point of fact, in his autobiography of 1876, that on the whole he did still believe in a sort of God, though not the God of the Christians, when he wrote the *Origin of Species* (*Autobiography*, p. 93). Total unbelief did not come till later.

This progression from naive faith to abandonment of religion was one of the ground-notes of his private experience, always with the added dimension of flying in the face of his wife's desires for him. They were undergoing divergent evolution. The other ground-note was his estrangement from the arts. The history of this, not the fact itself but the stages by which it was accomplished, is difficult to pin down. Darwin says in his autobiography that "up to the age of 30," which would bring him to the year of his marriage, "or beyond," he loved poetry and specifically Milton, Gray, Bryon, Wordsworth, Coleridge, Shelley, and Shakespeare (p. 138). Now for many years he had not been able to "endure" a line of poetry and Shakespeare least of all. His old taste for pictures and music had equally deserted him. "Music generally sets me thinking too energetically on what I have been at work on, instead of giving me pleasure" (p. 138). The only art works that meant anything to him in his prime were novels read aloud by his womenfolk and stipulated to have happy endings, dear lovable women in them, and no aftertaste. Of these he says with characteristic precision of speech that they were a "wonderful relief" to him (pp. 138–139). He took novels as a sedative to put his jangling nerves and churning thoughts to sleep. Great novels making great demands he did not relish. As his contemporary George Eliot went on making her tragic vision more intense and her art more powerful, she continually declined in Darwin's favor (*Life and Letters*, II, 305; III, 40).

With this falling away from great art, Darwin associated a general loss of power to feel intensely. He had experienced a decline in his fondness for fine scenery, which he says in 1876 has lasted longer than any other source of aesthetic gratification but "does not cause me the exquisite delight which it formerly did" (*Autobiography*, p. 138). Worse still, he thought he had lost the power of loving friends deeply. "Whilst I was young and strong I was capable of very warm attachments, but of late years, though I still have very friendly feelings towards many persons, I have lost the power of becoming deeply at-

tached to anyone, not even so deeply to my good and dear
friends Hooker and Huxley, as I should formerly have been"
(*Autobiography*, p. 115). He took no pleasure in this stripping
bare of his personality, so that the thinking machine cast off the
flesh that clothed it. "The loss of these tastes is a loss of happiness, and may possibly be injurious to the intellect, and more
probably to the moral character, by enfeebling the emotional
part of our nature."

II

Why did Darwin experience this atrophy of the aesthetic instincts? At least once he implied that he saw himself as Blake
and Wordsworth might have seen him, murdering to dissect, a
type of the analytical man who set the atomizing vision of
science above the integrating vision of art. "At last I fell fast
asleep on the grass, and awoke with a chorus of birds singing
around me, and squirrels running up the trees, and some wood-
peckers laughing, and it was as pleasant and rural a scene as ever
I saw, and I did not care one penny how any of the beasts or
birds had been formed" (*Life and Letters*, II, 114). This was
written on the only kind of vacation from science that he ever
permitted himself, an occasional short visit to a hydropathic
establishment to repair the "horrid state" of his stomach induced by steady work. Once he was out from under the burden
of science, he could see nature whole again and recover the
posture of Wordsworth. But he always buckled his burden back
on and headed for the dark tunnel of ratiocination that blotted
out the light of common day. He was ratifying out of his own
experience the teaching of the poets, Wordsworth, Blake, and
Keats, but not Shelley, that a man could not run with them and
see as they did and be a scientist too—unweave the rainbow
and still expect the heart to leap up at the sight. It was an an-
tinomy that John Stuart Mill declined to be impaled upon. He
knew, he said, that clouds are "vapour of water, subject to all
the laws of vapours in a state of suspension," but he knew
equally that they were objects of beauty lit up by the sun, not
either-or but both together (*Autobiography*, p. 107).

The healing and integral nature that Mill submitted to but
Darwin put from himself dwelt in the domesticated landscapes
of England. As a young man Darwin had gone voyaging on the

Beagle into some of the most untamed landscapes in the world
—from the bleak arid plains of Patagonia, too dour for human
comfort, to the "great wild, untidy, luxuriant hothouse" of the
Brazilian forest, which overshot the mark in the opposite direction.[4] These landscapes from another world—he so describes
them, as the nearest thing to visiting another planet—Darwin
could never put out of mind. They stood for a quite determinate
thing in his life-history: his most powerful experience of "the
sublime." This old category, rendered classic by Longinus and
refurbished in the eighteenth century by numerous hands, including Edmund Burke, is the most common piece of aesthetic
terminology in Darwin's writings from youth into age.[5] He was
still puzzling over the exact signification of it and simultaneously throwing it about with abandon in the 1870's. The two
things in his experience which had the most power to trigger an
access of sublimity were scenic grandeur, as in mountains and
forests, and great music, always epitomized for him by the
Messiah. "I felt glad I was alone," he said, on top of the Andes,
"it was like watching a thunderstorm, or hearing a chorus of
the Messiah in full orchestra" (*Beagle*, p. 394). What did the
Hallelujah Chorus and the view from the Andes have in common? What did Darwin mean by "the sublime"? He never did
give a straightforward definition, but one thing is clear. The
sublime was associated by Darwin with an upwelling from the
depths of the spirit that appeared to set reason aside and prevail
over it. This, at any rate, was in keeping with Longinus' formula
that the sublime is above and beyond the mere "persuasive"—
compelling assent by no logical sequence of propositions but by
immediate conviction. No wonder Darwin's sublime encom-
passed powerful incitements to religion. Sublime scenery as he
witnessed it on his voyage around the world induced in him
reverence, devotion, and worship. Great art by association with
scenic grandeur, scenic grandeur with religion, and all three
with the sublime, became part of a single universe of experience. "The state of mind," he says, "which grand scenes formerly excited in me, and which was intimately connected with
a belief in God, did not essentially differ from that which is

[4] *Journal of Researches into the Geology and Natural History of the
various countries visited by H.M.S. Beagle* (London, 1839), pp. 590, 604.
[5] On the concept of the sublime, see Marjorie Hope Nicolson, *Mountain Gloom and Mountain Glory* (Ithaca, N.Y., 1959).

often called the sense of sublimity" and brings to mind "the powerful though vague and similar feelings excited by music" (*Autobiography*, pp. 91–92). And again: music arouses the feelings of tenderness and love "which readily pass into devotion." [6] The mature Darwin moved away from art because he was continually moving away from religion.

The mainspring of Darwin's aversion from religion is unmistakable. He saw in religion what James and John Stuart Mill saw, assent to the evil of the world and acquisecence in it. To understand the form in which Darwin chiefly apprehended evil, it is necessary to juxtapose the peculiarities of his personal situation with the character of the age he lived in. As a boy he was encouraged by his father's example to hate the sight of blood and the practice of bleeding. As a medical student in Edinburgh, he had felt a "vivid" distress in walking the wards and rushed away in horror from blundering operations. From soon after his marriage till his death more than forty years later, he was a chronic sufferer from headaches, nausea, and stomach upsets. He had always been sensitive to pain. Now he came to live with it as an evil immediately perceived from within. It was all the more an evil for the monumental circumscription of pain that was going forward in Darwin's own lifetime. This took the double form of efforts at the mitigation or removal of pain and the pursuit of new occasions for sympathy with it. Darwin witnessed the introduction of anaesthesia and modern narcotics, the abolition of slavery and serfdom in the Western world, and the birth of organized movements for kindness to animals and children. The "blessed discovery" of chloroform, by which he had out five "grinders" at one time and hardly felt a thing, made him very happy for his children's sake (*Life and Letters*, I, 385). On the evils of slavery, always linked in his mind with the screams heard in Brazil and for ever after in his own nightmares, he was absolutely intransigent. Affection for Asa Gray did not keep him from saying plainly that people in England would never see anything to choose between North and South till the Northern cause was indissolubly bound up with abolition; and the only harsh words he is ever known to have addressed to any of his children were spoken to a son who appeared to be apologizing for the brutal conduct of the infa-

[6] *The Descent of Man* (London, 1871), II, 335.

mous Governor Eyre in Jamaica (*Life and Letters*, II, 377; III, 52–53). He was almost equally incensed about cruelty to animals, now first looming up as an unpardonable offense against civilization.

His concern for animals effected a powerful conjunction between the assault on pain and the accomplishment of Darwin's life-work. The discovery in animals of a whole new realm of objects to be felt for, sentimentalized over, and safeguarded from harm was a fundamental, and may have been a necessary, part of the environment in which the doctrine of evolution was established. It was no accident that Darwin lived in an age when Sir Edwin Landseer and Rosa Bonheur were among the most widely admired painters and the organized movement for kindness to animals got under way. It was no accident either that the people portrayed by his contemporary Dickens in *Hard Times* as having found the secret of being fully human were circus performers living on easy terms of companionability with learned dogs and horses and actually constituting with them a single economic and social unit. Darwin and all England with him, and a good deal of the rest of the civilized world besides, were conditioned as never before to accept their kinship with animals. The strategy of a man like Bishop Wilberforce, who tried to undermine the doctrine of evolution by seizing upon the postulated link to animals, could hardly have been more inept. The great apes no doubt were not very widely kept or loved in England, and it would have been better if Darwin had been able to say that men were descended from horses or dogs or better still the Monarch of the Glen, but the general idea of welcoming man's poor relations into the fold of human sympathies had already prevailed. When Darwin sprang from his carriage and fiercely berated a stranger for beating a horse, he was enacting one of the principal reasons for his inevitable triumph over his critics (*Life and Letters*, II, 200).

Not surprisingly, he took an equivocal position on the one matter where the current was superficially flowing in the other direction from the awakening of tenderness: the mushrooming recourse to vivisection by scientific investigators. Darwin did not deny that, properly guarded against abuse, it had an essential role to play in physiology. That did not change the fact that the practice made him personally "sick with horror" and he could not speak too harshly of men who engaged in it out of a "mere damnable and detestable curiosity" (*Life and Letters*, II, 200–201). As a result of these profoundly divided feelings, he initially lent his countenance to the disastrous view that moderate restraints upon vivisection by Parliament would be desirable, only to find that the restraints actually imposed (in 1876) were not moderate and not desirable. Yet even in retreat from his earlier position that legislation could do some good and no harm, he was motivated by his aversion from pain. Vivisection, humanely managed by the conscience of the investigator, would have to be tolerated precisely because it might produce new "remedies for pain and disease" in men and animals alike. He would sanction even pain to put pain to flight.

The raw sensitivity to pain which made Darwin a man of his age, and the fellow-feeling with animals which helped to make him the great vindicator of evolution, afford a clue to his alienation from the best literature of his time, symbolized in his not-so-joking remark that there ought to be a law against novels with unhappy endings. The power which great tragic novels have to raise a storm in the spirit that can never be laid again —their permanent heightening of sensitivity—he could not bear but sought instead for a dampening of consciousness by literature that left no trace behind; ephemeral and conducive to repose. He was in the position of James Mill and J. A. Roebuck, who felt so deeply that they could not imagine that others would experience a dearth of feeling and for themselves wished rather to hold it in check. In the circumstances Darwin could not possibly enter into the younger Mill's vindication of art as an emotional stimulus to the unfeeling. Darwin was trying to cut down on his emotional intake; and according to his own testimony, had considerable success in weaning himself from the rich diet of his youth and learning to feel more dimly. His turning away from art was both a means to this success and a token of it. It was a token as well of the fires within him that he was conscious of having to bank down.

Intense feeling was undesirable in Darwin's own experience as exacerbating his already keen sensitivities. It was or could be undesirable in a cosmic view as well. Therein lay a tremendous ambiguity at the very heart of Darwin's position. Natural selection itself proceeds by pain, suffering, frustration, and unfulfillment—the whole gamut that failure of promise encompasses. Any good that comes *of* it, comes *by* evil. Darwin could not deny, in fact he had to insist, that failure was stalking the world and performing grim labors. If the grim labors were to slacken or failure not to take its toll, natural selection would be by so much impeded. Darwin points in the *Descent of Man* to many dysgenic factors in civilized life by which those who would otherwise go under in the struggle for survival and procreation are kept afloat by the rest, often at the direct expense of the latter: exemption of the physically inferior from warfare, with conscription of the strongest young men to die in battle and leave few or no heirs behind them; public assistance to the poor; organized solicitude for the "imbecile" and "maimed"; and universal extension of medical benefits, so that to take only one example, thousands of people who would have succumbed to smallpox by reason of their weak constitutions have been spared to become fathers of the race.[7] Except for the policy on conscription, which is partly pragmatic as well as compassionate, all of these dysgenic factors arise out of tenderness for the weak. The implication is clear that tenderness has become a clog upon evolution. It was not always thus. Darwin in the *Descent of Man* can be seen looking wistfully back to some indistinct but shining age in the past, a moment of poise between two extremes, when men had learned to value social solidarity but had not yet confused this with tenderness for what he calls "the imbecile, the maimed, and other useless members of society" (*Descent of Man*, I, 103). One catches a momentary glimpse of Darwin's Wagnerian or Carlylean self peeping shyly out from under his invalid's cloak, where such things are often most at home, and yearning for the brave old forest days when the world was bathed in a stern but golden light and men were faithful to comrades, obedient to leaders, and strangers to pity. Good actions were those requiring "self-sacrifice, self-command, and the power of endurance" to further the ends of the tribe rather than the happiness of the individual members (*Descent of Man*, I, 95). Darwin hints that the light that shone in other

---

[7] *Descent of Man*, 2d ed. (London, 1874), cited from 2-volume edition (London, 1888), I, 206–207. The entire argument, except for conscription, in 1st ed. (London, 1871), I, 167–170. Unless otherwise indicated references will be to the latter edition.

days might come again if men would take as their object, not
the furtherance of individual happiness, but the promotion of
the "general good," defined as "the means by which the greatest
possible number of individuals can be reared in full vigour and
health, with all their faculties perfect, under the conditions to
which they are exposed" (Descent of Man, I, 98). But, he adds,
rather delightfully, such a procedure might "perhaps require
some limitation on account of political ethics."

III

Darwin remained in his central being a deeply sensitive man,
shrinking back from the spectacle of pain in other creatures,
and wishing to offer some alleviation. What could this consistently be for the great proponent of natural selection? One
answer was to refrain from positive acts of cruelty oneself and
try to get others to refrain. More profoundly, Darwin's answer
consisted in his repudiation of religion. This is the animus behind his unflagging interest in the theological interpretation of
his doctrines. If natural selection were to be construed, as his
great friend Asa Gray in America urged, as God's instrument
of continuous creation, then there was an overmastering Will
in the world that pain and evil should exist, if only to some
further end. They were not mere existents, they were existents
willed from on high. This to the shrinking and wincing Darwin
was an intolerable conception of the universe, shared by all religions alike. People kept telling him that to conjoin belief in
God with belief in natural selection merely went to deepen
their faith and enlarge the consolations of religion.[8] To him, a
God that dwelt in natural selection would be the worst of all
possible Gods. For the proprietor of the universe to have to seek
for a mere preponderance of good over evil in the world that he
made, which was the best that could be said for any progress
attained by natural selection, was monstrous in Darwin's eyes.
He did not want a God that had to proceed by Benthamite
calculus and either did not know how or did not care enough
to decree uncontaminated good. In a sense, he belonged, with
the Mills, to a class of God-deniers who were yearning after a
better God than God. How high their standard was in these
matters can be judged from the fact that Darwin thought there

[8] See, e.g., Mrs. Boole to Darwin, ca. 1867; Life and Letters, III, 63–65.

was a decided over-balance of happiness as against misery among sentient beings. He expressly says that the world is on the whole a good world—for "if all the individuals of any species were habitually to suffer to an extreme degree they would neglect to propagate their kind," but we have no evidence of this (*Autobiography*, pp. 88–90). Yet much intermittent suffering does occur; and this is sufficient in Darwin's opinion to condemn the idea of an "intelligent first cause" beyond any appeal to the admittedly greater quantity of habitual happiness. Moreover, he says that even if we are willing (as he was not) to accept the traditional Christian view that all evils suffered by men can be discounted as opportunities for spiritual improvement, the pain experienced by animals would remain an unanswerable reproach to any deity that presided over it: "the number of men in the world is as nothing compared with that of all other sentient beings, and these often suffer greatly without any moral improvement. A being so powerful and so full of knowledge as a God who could create the universe, is to our finite minds omnipotent and omniscient, and it revolts our understanding to suppose that his benevolence is not unbounded, for what advantage can there be in the sufferings of millions of the lower animals throughout almost endless time?" (*Autobiography*, p. 90). After God was discarded by Darwin, the suffering of the world remained undiminished; but he rightly intuited that modern man would rather have senseless suffering than suffering warranted to be intelligible because willed from on high. Darwin gave to his fellow men the best though terrible gift and comfort that he could devise: the assurance that the evil of the world was like the world itself, brute and ungrounded and ready to be stamped by each man with his own meaning and no other.

Here Darwin was sitting in judgment upon the tradition of natural theology, which sought to confer upon the universe the character of a work of art from the hand of the Great Artist; and more than this, sought to lend a common affective tone, a unifying vision of beauty, harmony, and fostering influences, to the universal landscape, so that all partial evils were lost in a greater good. This impulse to make a willed unity of disparate elements, to fuse parts into an emotional whole, is almost diagnostic for the artist's temperament. Natural selection was pre-

cisely the denial of nature as a planned work of art and an effort
to dissipate the pleasing affective tone that natural theologians
tried to lend it. It would be tempting to say that Darwin turned
against works of art because he had determined to smash the
greatest of all. At some deep level this may have operated; but
we are on safer ground if, while recognizing the profound con-
sonance between his revulsion from art and his repudiation of
natural theology, we emphasize Darwin's resolve not to be an
accomplice in the evil of the world by assenting to God's dominion.

We are brought round again to Darwin's experience of the
sublime and the triple conjunction in this thought of scenic
grandeur, music, and religion: all standing in common for the
uncontrollable motions in the spirit and cutting adrift from
reason which Darwin associated with the intimations of divin-
ity which came to him in the Brazilian forest. He had to believe
for his own comfort and the comfort of others that the instruction of the sublime in behalf of religion was false. Just so, the
surges of feeling that music could arouse were capable of arming
men for battle, but equally without any real bearing upon the
right and reason of their cause. The dominion of art, as of religion, is the dominion of the irrational. The association can be
documented from both ends of Darwin's career. At twenty-nine,
he spoke of getting up close to a painting and being laid open
by the "peculiar smell," presumably varnish, to the "old irrational ideas" that "thrilled across me" as an undergraduate in
the Fitzwilliam Museum at Cambridge.[9] Thirty-six years later,
in a moment of deep revelation in the *Descent of Man*, he
touched in immediate succession upon the gusts of emotion
that whip through a crowd of African Negroes, the excited chat-
tering of monkeys, and the "sensations and ideas" aroused in
modern man by music, which appear "from their vagueness, yet
depth, like mental reversions to the emotions and thoughts of a
long-past age."[10] Communion with primitive man and sub-
human relatives of man and reversion through music to the

[9] Entry of 12 Aug. 1838 in the unpublished Notebook 'M' in Cambridge University Library. I owe this quotation to the kindness of Dr.
Sydney Smith of St. Catharine's College, Cambridge.
[10] *Descent of Man* (London, 1888), II, 364–365. Negroes omitted in
1st ed.; relevant passage, II, 336.

dawn of history—it is an evocation in time and place of all occasions where feeling may be expected to prevail over reason or not even encounter any reason to put to rout. Response to music, like response to religion, does not give true evidence of anything except a will toward illusion. Music "arouses dormant sentiments of which we had not conceived the possibility, and do not know the meaning; or, as Richter says, tells us of things we have not seen and shall not see." [11] We are here in the general vicinity of Bentham's dictum that art is lies and has the power to certify lies and make them pass for truth. It was among the most terrible indictments that a man like Darwin could imagine, whose most distinctive quality was an instinct for truth-telling which has hardly ever been surpassed—has there ever been another scientist who included in his great book all the arguments against it that he could think of? He could only be true to himself by resisting the access of illusion wherever it tried to creep in.

In his resolve to be one of the great Truth-Bearers, Darwin strove to perfect himself as a fact-and-dust man, more abundant in learning and insight, more generous in spirit, and more divided than Thomas Gradgrind, but endeavoring to stand for the same thing and indeed opening out cosmic vistas for application of the Gradgrind philosophy. To deal, not in apt caricatures upon historical men, but in real men of heroic stature, Darwin was a kind of successor to the seventeenth-century Puritans with their terror of the imagination. To those who would resist its wiles, the Puritans held out in compensation the prospect of a sober and godly life. Redemption they could not promise. So too with Darwin. In repelling illusion, he was taking the only compassion upon his fellow-men that he could contrive and bestowing upon them the best though somber good that their situation permitted. The chief lie of lying religion for him was that evil could have been inflicted from on high instead of simply occurring. If, by access to the sublime, he should assent to this lie, his act of charity to mankind for uncovering the harsh necessity of natural selection would fall to

---

[11] *Descent of Man* (London, 1871), II, 336; the entire passage, including the quotation from Richter, quoted from Herbert Spencer. Cf. fn. 12 below.

the ground. Love of mankind and love of the truth combined with fear of religion to make Darwin suspicious of art, a type of the anaesthetic man, both in the literal sense of "not feeling" and in the derivative sense of taking steps to repress the pain that he was capable of feeling.

IV

His own anaesthetic state was mirrored forth in his scientific view of the world. As he had cut art out of his own life, so he left it out of his evolutionary scheme for mankind in the *Descent of Man*. In his only direct confrontation with Herbert Spencer, they took diametrically opposite views on the cosmic role of music. Spencer held that music followed speech in the evolutionary sequence as an "idealized language of emotion" and has been continually reacting upon ordinary language in the form of vocal modulation to produce a kind of running "commentary of the emotions upon the propositions of the intellect." [12] Men not only understand each other, they *feel* for each other to the extent that this language of emotions is perfected. Spencer looks to the day when perfection will be attained. We may expect, he says, that the language of feelings will ultimately enable men to partake "completely" of one another's emotions. It is a prospect of universal good-will born of music and fed by music. For Darwin the role of music in the history of the world has long since been outworn.[13] He held, in direct contradiction to Spencer, that music preceded speech and gave birth to it. Once this occurred, music had outlived its cosmic function except as a means of courtship among birds. In the life of men, music is now a mere epiphenomenon, a froth on the surface of life: "neither the enjoyment nor the capacity of producing musical notes are faculties of the least direct use to man in reference to his ordinary habits of life" (*Descent of Man*, II, 333). He even went on to say that this useless attribute "must be ranked among the most mysterious" with which man is endowed. Here, in his eagerness to put down the pre-

[12] Herbert Spencer, "The Origin and Function of Music" (1857); in *Essays, Scientific, Political, and Speculative* (New York, 1891), II, 419, 422.
[13] *Descent of Man* (London, 1888), II, 355–367; slightly amended from 1st ed., II, 330–337.

tensions of music, Darwin was underestimating the power of his own teaching. He had supplied a perfectly plausible account of the *emergence* of poetry, singing, dancing, and love of ornamentation, as rooted in sexual selection. He had even assigned to music in the distant past the tremendous cosmic function of generating language. What he had failed to do was to suggest of what use the fine arts might be in the present and for the long future; why in their "mysterious" way they should stubbornly endure and grow more potent instead of shrivelling up into rudimentary organs like the appendix.

Historical circumstances conspired to make Darwin's great refusal of significance to the arts less glaring. He died in 1882, before the major works of prehistoric sculpture and painting had been authenticated. Though engraved pieces of bone were being uncovered by Edouard Lartet from the early 1860's forward, Sir Charles Lyell in his *Antiquity of Man* of 1863 always meant by "work of art" an artifact; and the incredible cave paintings of Altamira, though actually discovered at the end of the '70's, were not given a clean bill of authenticity by the principal skeptic till 1902. Darwin did refer in the second and last edition of the *Descent* in 1874 to the discovery by Lartet of two flutes made of bone, but these did not have the power to project artistic expression into the very center of prehistoric life as the great mural paintings did.[14] If one could imagine a slight speeding up in the history of archaeology—which is probably excluded by the fact that the cave paintings required for their acceptance at true value precisely the steeping of an entire generation in Darwinism—Darwin would have been confronted with a grave spiritual crisis. If driven to it, he would not have been at a loss to imagine a cosmic function for art. That was the trouble. He had a solution all too ready at hand but one that would have been intolerable to him as a human being. The iron band that clamped art, sublimity, and religion together in his own experience would have meant that the obvious way to build art into his system would be to assign a powerful role to religion as a constructive force in the development of mankind. Despite one or two equivocal tributes to religion as the mainstay of morality but also superstition, the last thing that Darwin wanted to do

[14] *Descent of Man* (London, 1888), II, 362.

was to attribute any lasting evolutionary significance to it.

John Stuart Mill, if he had been charged with drawing up an evolutionary scheme, would not have lain under the same inhibition. For him the arts energized indeterminately, they did not confine him to a single channel and that unwelcome, or make him "recreant" to his prior commitments, but infused these with emotional gratification without in any way pitching him into the arms of religion (*Autobiography*, p. 101). He was not turned about in his course but sped rejoicing on his way. That was part of what Dickens had been trying to say about Louisa Gradgrind. By openness to works and endeavors of the imagination, she would have been "wiser, happier, more loving, more contented, more innocent and human" and persuaded that life was "worth the pain and trouble of a contest." But even at the end of the book, when she had begun to be human, she continued to lead the same domestic life as before. She did not find a new calling but new courage and zest to prosecute the old. Significantly, Dickens nowhere attributes to her any yearning after religion or ultimate conversion to it. The instrument of her redemption, Sissy Jupe, is like Mill's Helen Taylor in not even proffering solicitations to conversion.

Darwin was menaced by conversion from within and without. That was the irreducible difference between him and his wife, with her discreet endeavors at bringing him around and silent dissent from his deepening unbelief; and that, above all, was the menace of art. *He* would be turned about by art, manacled to religion, and diverted from his role in history. For the humane import of the doctrine of evolution through natural selection was to lop off the Godhead and show how biological order could be generated without a divine fiat. He could only keep upon his course and be the fit author of his own revolution by burking the evolutionary significance of the arts.

It was an omission that has never been fully repaired. Only one voice since Darwin has spoken with comparable force to the biological situation of man; and though Sigmund Freud took ample account of the arts as a fundamental human activity, he failed equally with Darwin to attribute to them any desirable function in evolution. With some qualifications, he tended to regard the arts as a strategy of concealment by which men attempted to evade the truth about their own nature, to wrap it up in symbols. If Freud had believed with Eugene O'Neill and others in the healing and saving power of illusion, he might have seen in this an aid to survival and increment of fitness. On the contrary, he regarded art as being in this character regressive, a means of turning away from reality to the pleasure principle. It was his own office to make men behold the truth about themselves in its naked aspect with a steady and unflinching regard; and health of mind lay in the scrutiny. Freud could not correct the bias in Darwin. They were at one in their mistrust of the arts as fostering illusion. As their common heirs, we still lack a universally compelling vision of science and art as reenforcing each other and flourishing together, not as truth locked in battle with illusion but as clarity of intellect joined to warmth of feeling.

WILLIAM BUTLER YEATS

Edmund Wilson

The author of "The Lake Isle of Innisfree," which had so delighted Robert Louis Stevenson, had grown, in an interval of ten years during which nobody outside of Ireland had apparently paid much attention to him, to the unmistakable stature of a master. No other poet writing English in our time has been able to deal with supreme artistic success with such interesting and such varied experience. No other writer has been able to sustain the traditional grand manner of the poet with so little effect of self-consciousness.

And in spite of the immense amount of poetry published and read to-day, the personality truly and naturally poetic seems to be becoming rarer and rarer. It may be true that the kind of dignity and distinction which have been characteristic of the

From Edmund Wilson, *Axel's Castle*, pp. 26–63. Copyright 1931 by Charles Scribner's Sons; renewal copyright 1959 by Edmund Wilson. Reprinted by permission of Charles Scribner's Sons.

poet in the past are becoming more and more impossible in our modern democratic society and during a period when the ascendancy of scientific ideas has made man conscious of his kinship with other animals and of his subjection to biological and physical laws rather than of his relation to the gods. It was easy for the lyric poet, from Wyatt's age to Waller's, to express himself both directly and elegantly, because he was a courtier, or, in any case, a member of a comparatively small educated class, whose speech combined the candor and naturalness of conversation among equals with the grace of a courtly society. It was possible for him honestly to take up a residence in an intellectual world where poetic images stood for actualities because the scientific language and technique for dealing with these actualities had not yet come to permeate thought. But the modern poet who would follow this tradition, and who would yet deal with life in any large way, must create for himself a special personality, must maintain a state of mind, which shall shut out or remain indifferent to many aspects of the contemporary world. This necessity accounts partly, I suppose, for Yeats's preoccupation in his prose writings with what he calls the Mask or Anti-Self, a sort of imaginary personality, quite antagonistic to other elements of one's nature, which the poet must impose upon himself. It is hard to imagine a seventeenth-century poet being driven to such a theory—a theory which makes one's poetic self figure as one of the halves of a split personality; and it seems true that Yeats himself has not been able to keep up his poetic role without a certain effort..We find, at any rate, in his criticism and his autobiographical writings a remarkably honest and illuminating account of the difficulties of remaining a poet during the age in which we live.

Yeats seems to be conscious from the first of an antagonism between the actual world of industry, politics and science, on the one hand, and the imaginative poetic life, on the other. He tells us, in his autobiography, that a vital issue seemed to be raised for him, in his boyhood, by the then popular and novel realism of Bastien-Lepage and Carolus Durand as against the mysticism of the Pre-Raphaelite painters. Bastien-Lepage's "clownish peasant staring with vacant eyes at her great boots" represented already to the young Yeats that Naturalistic, scientific vision which contradicted and warred with his own. And he takes up from the beginning, in his criticism, a definite and explicit position in regard to Naturalism: he will stand apart from the democratic, the scientific, modern world—his poetic life shall be independent of it; his art shall owe nothing to its methods. His principles in literature are those of the Symbolists, but he formulates them more clearly and defends them with more vigor than anyone else has yet done in English.

"There is," he asserts in his early essay on the symbolism of Shelley, "for every man some one scene, some one adventure, some one picture, that is the image of his secret life, for wisdom first speaks in images and . . . this one image, if he would but brood over it his whole life long, would lead his soul, disentangled from unmeaning circumstance and the ebb and flow of the world, into that far household, where the undying gods await all whose souls have become simple as flame, whose bodies have become quiet as an agate lamp." All great literature, says Yeats, is created out of symbols: observations and statistics mean nothing; works of art which depend upon them can have no enduring value. "There is something," he says, "of an old wives' tale in fine literature. The makers of it are like an old peasant telling stories of the great famine or the hangings of '98 or from his own memories. He has felt something in the depth of his mind and he wants to make it as visible and powerful to our senses as possible. He will use the most extravagant words or illustrations if they will suit his purpose. Or he will invent a wild parable, and the more his mind is on fire or the more creative it is, the less will he look at the outer world or value it for its own sake. It gives him metaphors and examples, and that is all. He is even a little scornful of it, for it seems to him while the fit is on that the fire has gone out of it and left it but white ashes. I cannot explain it, but I am certain that every high thing was invented in this way, between sleeping and waking, as it were, and that peering and peeping persons are but hawkers of stolen goods. How else could their noses have grown so ravenous or their eyes so sharp?"

And in all his activity as playwright and journalist in connection with the Abbey Theatre, Yeats is leading a reaction against Naturalism. This reaction, which, by way of Germany

and under the name of Expressionism, has attracted so much
more attention since the War, had not, at the time of the
founding of the Abbey Theatre, manifested itself very vigorously on the Continent. Symbolism did not play yet in the
theatre the role that it was playing in poetry. Yet its seeds had
already sprouted here and there. August Strindberg, returning
from Paris to Sweden, wrote between 1899 and 1902 the Symbolistic "To Damascus" and "Dream Play," the prototypes of
the German Expressionistic drama; and Maeterlinck, with
vague, pale and suave images, quite different from Strindberg's
lively, queer and dissonant ones, had created quite a little theatre of Symbolism. Now Yeats, in his own dramatic works, has
produced a theatre somewhat similar to Maeterlinck's. The productions of a greater poet, equipped with a richer and more
solid mythology, these plays do, however, take place in the same
sort of twilit world as Maeterlinck's—a world in which the characters are less often dramatic personalities than disembodied
broodings and longings.

Yeats at this period, the period of the founding and the first
battles of the Abbey Theatre, is both active and effective. There
has always been more of the public figure and more of the pug-
nacious Irishman about him than his philosophy invites us to
believe. But this philosophy never ceases to insist upon the irreconcilable opposition between the life of self-assertion in the
practical world and the life consecrated to the recovery and
contemplation of the precious symbol, which, "if he (the poet)
would but brood over it his whole life long, would lead his soul,
disentangled from unmeaning circumstances and the ebb and
flow of the world," into the presence of the gods.

For the rest, Yeats's prose, in its beginnings, when he is most
under the influence of the Pre-Raphaelites and Pater, is a little
self-consciously archaic—it has a Renaissance elaborateness and
pomposity; and it is a little too close to the language of poetry
—the meaning is often clotted by metaphor. But Yeats's prose,
like his verse, has, with time, undergone a discipline and
emerged with a clearer outline. Yeats is to-day a master of prose
as well as a great poet. He was already magnificent in his inter-
mediate period—the period of "Per Amica Silentia Lunae"
(1917): "We make out of the quarrel with others rhetoric, but

of the quarrel with ourselves, poetry. Unlike the rhetoricians, who get a confident voice from remembering the crowd they have won or may win, we sing amid our uncertainty; and, smitten even in the presence of the most high beauty by the knowledge of our solitude, our rhythm shudders. I think, too, that no fine poet, no matter how disordered his life, has ever, even in his mere life, had pleasure for his end. Nor has any poet I have read of or heard of or met with been a sentimentalist. The other self, the anti-self or the antithetical self, as one may choose to name it, comes but to those who are no longer deceived, whose passion is reality. The sentimentalists are practical men who believe in money, in position, in a marriage bell, and whose understanding of happiness is to be so busy whether at work or at play, that all is forgotten but the momentary aim. They find their pleasure in a cup that is filled from Lethe's wharf, and for the awakening, for the vision, for the revelation of reality, tradition offers us a different word—ecstasy."

Yeats has shown himself, in his prose writings, a man of both exceptionally wide information and exceptional intellectual curiosity, but, for all the variety of his interests and the versatility of his intelligence, he has, in rejecting the methods of modern science, cut himself off in a curious way from the general enlightened thought of his time. Yet his mind is so comprehensive and so active that he has felt the need of constructing a system: and, finding it impossible to admit the assumptions upon which most modern systems are based, he has had recourse to the only science which his position has allowed him to accept, the obsolete science of Astrology. As a young man, Yeats frequented clairvoyants and students of Astrology and Magic; Madame Blavatsky, the necromantic Theosophist, seems to have made upon him a considerable impression. And in 1901 he was led to formulate, in an essay on Magic, the following set of beliefs, to which he still apparently adheres:

(1) That the borders of our mind are ever shifting, and that many minds can flow into one another, as it were, and create or reveal a single mind, a single energy.

(2) That the borders of our memories are as shifting, and that our memories are a part of one great memory, the memory of

Nature herself.

(3) That this great mind and great memory can be evoked by symbols.

What Yeats was really approaching here was some such systematic study of the symbolism of myths, trances, dreams and other human visions as psychoanalysis and anthropolgy were attempting from a different direction. And despite the obvious charlatanism or naïveté of most of his instructors and fellow investigators, Yeats's account of his researches is interesting. For it is not merely that Yeats loves the marvellous: he is also intent upon discovering symbols which may stand for the elements of his own nature or which shall seem to possess some universal significance. The results of this research are very curious. When we read Yeats's account of his adventures among the mediums, it becomes plain that, in spite of his repudiation of science, he has always managed to leave himself a margin of scientific doubt. Like Huysmans, he betrays an instinct to scrutinize and check up on the supernatural which is disastrous to genuine mysticism. Just as in Huysmans's case, we always feel that the wistful student of Satanism has too much solid Dutch common sense really to deceive himself about his devils, so in Yeats—he himself has confessed it—the romantic amateur of Magic is always accompanied and restrained by the rationalistic modern man. "He and I often quarreled," Yeats writes of himself and A.E., "because I wanted him to examine and question his visions, and write them out as they occurred; and still more because I thought symbolic what he thought real like the men and women that had passed him on the road." Yet Huysmans went so far as to claim—or at least to make one of his characters claim—as genuine examples of demoniacal possession those very hysteria cases of Charcot's which at that moment were leading Charcot's young pupil Freud to his first great discovery of the principle of emotional repression; and Yeats attributes to a sort of supernatural being designated as "Anima Mundi" precisely such universal symbols as are studied by such psychologists as Jung. What is most curious is that Yeats should at last have constructed out of these symbols an elaborate mystical-metaphysical system.

This system was set forth in "A Vision," a work which occupied Yeats for many years and which he published privately in 1926. "A Vision" presented an elaborate theory of the variation of human personality, of the vicissitudes of human history and of the transformations of the soul in this world and the next. This theory was worked out with geometrical diagrams and set forth in terms of such unfamiliar conceptions as *daimons, tinctures, cones, gyres, husks* and *passionate bodies.*

Yeats asserts that human personality follows the pattern of a "Great Wheel." That is, the types of personality possible constitute a kind of closed circle—they are regular stages in a circular journey to and fro between complete objectivity at one pole and complete subjectivity at the other; and this journey may be represented by the orbit of the moon, to which it corresponds. Let the moon represent subjectivity and the sun, objectivity: then the dark of the moon, when it is closest to the sun, is the phase of complete objectivity; and the full moon, which is farthest from the sun, is the phase of complete subjectivity. At these two poles of the circle, human life is impossible: there exist only antipodal types of supernatural beings. But along the circumference of the circle, between these two ultra-human poles, there occur twenty-six phases which cover all possible types of human personality.

Yeats's theory of the variation of these types is extremely complicated. He begins by assigning to "incarnate man" four "Faculties": the Will, "by which is understood feeling that has not become desire . . . an energy as yet uninfluenced by thought, action or emotion"; the Mask, which means "the image of what we wish to become, or of that to which we give our reverence"; the Creative Mind, "the intellect . . . all the mind that is consciously constructive"; and the Body of Fate, "the physical and mental environment, the changing human body, the stream of Phenomena as this affects a particular individual, all that is forced upon us from without." The Will is always opposite the Mask: "it looks into a painted picture." The Creative Mind is opposite the Body of Fate: "it looks into a photograph; but both look into something which is the opposite of themselves." We follow the Will around the clock, and by combining it with the other elements according to geometrical laws we calculate the characters of the different phases. Starting at the right of the objective pole, the soul passes through varieties of almost purely physical life—Yeats takes his examples here from the Bacchuses and shepherds of the poets. It is moving toward subjectivity, however—Walt Whitman, Alexandre Dumas: it is seeking itself, and as it progresses, it becomes more beautiful. The ultra-human subjective phase, which apparently includes Christ, is described as "a phase of complete beauty," where "Thought and Will are indistinguishable, effort and attainment are indistinguishable—nothing is apparent but dreaming Will and the Image that it dreams." This is preceded and followed by phases which include Baudelaire and Beardsley; Keats and Giorgione; Blake and Rabelais; Dante and Shelley; and presumably Yeats himself: men who have withdrawn from the life of the world in order to live in their dream. But once the all-subjective phase is past, the soul

> . . . would be the world's servant, and as it serves,
> Choosing whatever task's most difficult
> Among tasks not impossible, it takes
> Upon the body and upon the soul
> The coarseness of the drudge. Before the full
> It sought itself and afterwards the world.

And it is now leaving beauty behind and headed toward deformity:

> Reformer, merchant, statesman, learned man,
> Dutiful husband, honest wife by turn,
> Cradle upon cradle, and all in flight and all
> Deformed because there is no deformity
> But saves us from a dream.

The soul has now come full circle: the three final human phases before the phase of complete objectivity are the Hunchback, the Saint and the Fool.

Yeats has worked all this out with great care and with considerable ingenuity. He has described each of the twenty-eight phases and supplied us with typical examples. What we find in this part of the book is Yeats's familiar preoccupation with the conflict between action and philosophy, reality and imagination. (It is amusing and characteristic that, according to his system, the side of humanity closest to the sun—that is, closest the objective nature—should be the side that is bathed in darkness, whereas the side which is furthest from the sun—that is, nearest the subjective nature—should be the side that is bright!) Now this is a subject which has hitherto, in Yeats's prose as well as in his verse, usually inspired him well; the symbols of the Mask, the Sun and Moon, etc., if they have sometimes been a little disconcerting when we encountered them in his critical writings, have created just the right impression of significance in mystery for Symbolistic poetry. And there are, to be sure, certain passages of "A Vision" as brilliant as Yeats at his best. He writes, for example, of the phase of "the Receptive Man," to which he assigns Rembrandt and Synge: "The man wipes his breath from the window pane, and laughs in his delight at all the varied scene." And of the phase of "the Obsessed Man," to which he assigns Giorgione and Keats: "When we compare these images with those of any subsequent phase, each seems studied for its own sake; they float as in serene air, or lie hidden in some valley, and if they move it is to music that returns always to the same note, or in a dance that so returns upon itself that they seem immortal." And, in what is perhaps the most eloquent passage in the book, he returns to a certain type of beautiful uncontemplative woman who has already haunted his poetry: "Here are born those women who are most touching in their beauty. Helen was of this phase; and she comes before the mind's eye elaborating a delicate personal discipline as though she would make her whole life an image of a unified *antithetical* (that is, subjective) energy. While seeming an image of softness, and of quiet, she draws perpetually upon glass with a diamond. Yet she will not number among her sins anything that does not break that personal discipline, no matter what it may seem according to others' discipline; but if she fail in her own discipline she will not deceive herself, and for all the languor of her movements, and her indifference to the acts of others, her mind is never at peace. She will wander much alone as though she consciously meditated her masterpiece that shall be at the full moon, yet unseen by human eye, and when she returns to her house she will look upon her household with timid eyes, as though she knew that all power of self-protection had been taken away, and that of her once *primary Tincture* (that is, objective element) nothing remained but a strange irresponsible innocence. . . . Already perhaps, through weakness of desire, she understands nothing, while alone seeming of service. Is it not because she desires so little and gives so little that men will die and murder in her service?" And there is a strange imaginative power in the conception behind the final sequence of the Hunchback, the Saint and the Fool.

Yet "A Vision," when we try to read it, makes us impatient with Yeats. As a rule, he expounds his revelations as if he took them seriously—that is, as if he believed that *masks* and *husks* and *daimons* and *passionate bodies* were things which actually existed, as if they were as real as those visions of A.E.'s which had been as real to A.E. as the people in the street, but which Yeats had tried to induce him to question; and indeed one would think that to elaborate a mystical system so complicated and so tedious, it would be necessary to believe in it pretty strongly. Yet now and then the skeptical Yeats reasserts himself and we are startled by an unexpected suggestion that, after all, the whole thing may be merely "a background for my thought, a painted scene." If the whole thing, we ask ourselves, has been merely an invented mythology, in which Yeats himself does not believe, what right has he to bore us with it—what right has he to expect us to explore page after page of such stuff as the following description of the habits of the soul after death: "The *Spirit* first floats horizontally within the man's dead body, but then rises until it stands at his head. The *Celestial Body* is also horizontal at first but lies in the opposite position, its feet where the *Spirit's* head is, and then rising, as does the *Spirit*, stands up at last at the feet of the man's body. The *Passionate Body* rises straight up from the genitals and stands in the centre. The *Husk* remains in the body until the time for it to be separated and lost in *Anima Mundi*."

In "A Packet for Ezra Pound" (1929) a new light is thrown on "A Vision." We learn that Yeats's wife is a medium, and that the theories set forth in this book were communicated through her by supernatural beings. Yeats tells us how, four days after their marriage in 1917, Mrs. Yeats surprised him by attempting automatic writing. "What came in disjointed sentences, in almost illegible writing, was so exciting, sometimes so profound, that I persuaded her to give an hour or two day after day to the unknown writer, and after some half-dozen such hours offered to spend what remained of life explaining and piecing together those scattered sentences. 'No,' was the answer, 'we have come to give you metaphors for poetry.' The unknown writer took his theme at first from my just published 'Per Amica Silentia Lunae.' I had made a distinction between the perfection that is from a man's combat with himself and that which is from a combat with circumstances, and upon this simple distinction he built up an elaborate classification of men according to their more or less complete expression of one type or the other. He supported his classification by a series of geometrical symbols and put these symbols in an order that answered the question in my essay as to whether some prophet could not prick upon the calendar the birth of a Napoleon or a Christ." Yeats describes the manifestations which accompanied these revelations: the perfumes, whistlings, smells of burnt feathers, bursts of music, apparitions of great black birds and of "persons in clothes of the late sixteenth century and of the seventeenth." On one occasion, when an owl was hooting in the garden, the dictating spirit asked for a recess: "Sounds like that," the spirit explained, "give us great pleasure." And there were also mischievous obstructive spirits who attempted to mislead the Yeatses and who were designated as "Frustrators"; "the automatic script would deteriorate, grow sentimental or confused, and when I pointed this out the communicator would say 'from such and such an hour, on such and such a day, all is frustration.' I would spread out the script and he would cross all out back to the answer that began it, but had I not divined frustration he would have said nothing."

We learn also, by the way, a fact which might, for a psychologist, throw a good deal of light on the development of Yeats' personality. It appears that not only has Yeats always succeeded in steering clear of science: he has never till recently read philosophy. "Apart from two or three of the

principal Platonic Dialogues I knew no philosophy. Arguments
with my father, whose convictions had been formed by John
Stuart Mill's attack upon Sir William Hamilton, had destroyed
my confidence and driven me from speculation to the direct
experience of the Mystics. I had once known Blake as
thoroughly as his unfinished confused Prophetic Books permitted, and I had read Swedenborg and Boehme, and my
initiation into the 'Hermetic Students' had filled my head with
Cabalistic imagery." Now, however, he wants to study philosophy as an aid to understanding the "system." The spirits
ask him to wait till they have finished. At the end of three
years, when the supernatural revelations have ceased, and "A
Vision" is actually in proof, Yeats takes down from Mrs.
Yeats, who, it appears, did not share her husband's ignorance,
a list of the philosophers she had read. For four years, Yeats
applies himself to these, and what he finds makes him uneasy
about "A Vision": he feels that he must partly have mis-
interpreted what the spirits have told him. But the spirits
themselves intervene to put an end to this disquieting situation:
they make him stop his philosophical studies.

As we read all this, we say to ourselves that Yeats, growing
older, has grown more credulous. But we come, at the end, to
the following passage: "Some will ask if I believe all that this
book contains, and I will not know how to answer. Does the
word belief, used as they will use it, belong to our age, can
I think of the world as there and I here judging it?" And he
intimates that, after all, his system may be only a set of
symbols like another—a set of symbols, we recognize, like the
Irish myths with which he began.

Into the personal situation suggested by Yeats's account of
his revelations, it is inappropriate and unnecessary to go: the
psychological situation seems plain. When Yeats, at the crucial
period of his life, attempted to leave fairyland behind, when
he became aware of the unsatisfying character of the life of
iridescent revery, when he completely recreated his style so
as to make it solid, homely and exact where it had formerly
been shimmering or florid—the need for dwelling with part of
his mind—or with his mind for part of the time—in a world
of pure imagination, where the necessities of the real world

do not hold, had, none the less, not been conjured away by the new artistic and intellectual habits he was cultivating. Where the early Yeats had studied Irish folk-lore, collected and sorted Irish fairy tales, invented fairy tales for himself, the later Yeats worked out from the mediumistic communications of his wife the twenty-eight phases of the human personality and the transformations of the soul after death. Yeats's sense of reality to-day is inferior to that of no man alive—indeed, his greatness is partly due precisely to the vividness of that sense. In his poetry, in his criticism and in his memoirs, it is the world we all live in with which we are confronted—the world we know, with all its frustrations, its defeats, its antagonisms and its errors—the mind that sees is not naïve, as the heart that feels is not insensitive. They meet reality with comprehension and with passion—but they have phases, we are astonished to discover, when they do not seem to meet it at all. Yet the scientific criticism of supernatural phenomena is actually as much a part of the reality of Yeats' world as it is of that of most of the rest of us. And when Yeats writes of his supernatural experiences, this criticism, though it may be kept in the background, is nevertheless always present—his realistic sense is too strong, his intellectual integrity too high, to leave it out of the picture. Though he is much addicted to these fantastic imaginings, though he no doubt needs their support to enable him to sustain his role of great poet—yet when he comes to write about his spirits and their messages, he cannot help letting us in on the imposture. He believes, but —he does not believe: the impossibility of believing is the impossibility which he accepts most reluctantly, but still it is there with the other impossibilities of this world which is too full of weeping for a child to understand.

It is interesting to compare "A Vision" with that other compendious treatise on human nature and destiny by that other great writer from Dublin: Bernard Shaw's "Guide to Socialism and Capitalism." Here we can see unmistakably the differences between the kind of literature which was fashionable before the War and the kind which has been fashionable since. Shaw and Yeats, both coming as young men to London from eighteenth-century Dublin, followed diametrically op-

posite courses. Shaw shouldered the whole unwieldy load of
contemporary sociology, politics, economics, biology, medicine
and journalism, while Yeats, convinced that the world of
science and politics was somehow fatal to the poet's vision, as
resolutely turned away. Shaw accepted the scientific technique
and set himself to master the problems of an industrial
democratic society, while Yeats rejected the methods of
Naturalism and applied himself to the introspective plumbing
of the mysteries of the individual mind. While Yeats was
editing Blake, Shaw was grappling with Marx; and Yeats was
appalled by Shaw's hardness and efficiency. "I hated it," he
says of "Arms and the Man"; "it seemed to me inorganic,
logical straightness and not the crooked road of life and I
stood aghast before its energy." And he tells us that Shaw
appeared to him in a dream in the form of a sewing machine,
"that clicked and shone, but the incredible thing was that the
machine smiled, smiled perpetually."

In his Great Wheel of the twenty-eight phases, Yeats has
situated Shaw at a phase considerably removed from his own,
and where the individual is headed straight for the deformity
of seeking, not the soul, but the world. And their respective
literary testaments—the "Vision" and the "Guide"—published
almost at the same time, mark the extreme points of their
divergence: Shaw bases all human hope and happiness on an
equal distribution of income, which he believes will finally
make impossible even the pessimism of a Swift or a Voltaire;
while Yeats, like Shaw a Protestant for whom the Catholic's
mysticism was impossible, has in "A Vision" made the life
of humanity contingent on the movements of the star. "The
day is far off," he concludes, "when the two halves of man
can divine each its own unity in the other as in a mirror, Sun
in Moon, Moon in Sun, and so escape out of the Wheel."

WHEN I HEARD THE LEARN'D ASTRONOMER

Walt Whitman

When I heard the learn'd astronomer,
When the proofs, the figures, were ranged in columns before me,
When I was shown the charts and diagrams, to add, divide, and measure them,
When I sitting heard the astonomer where he lectured with much applause in the lecture-room,
How soon unaccountable I became tired and sick,
Till rising and gliding out I wander'd off by myself,
In the mystical moist night-air, and from time to time,
Look'd up in perfect silence at the stars.

THOSE SKILLED BARBARIANS

William Barry Furlong

To those who've endured an engineering education, as I have, it is clear that the major fault of our engineers is not that they don't know what Shakespeare and Shaw are all about but that they don't know what science and engineering are all about. They lack not simply a world culture but the common culture of their own profession.

Why? Because so very few persons in engineering are equipped to provide it. Except for a few great and creative minds, the broad and calcified cross-section of engineering instructors bring to the classroom an almost invincible ignorance of their field's culture and how to teach it. They know little about the world of men or the world of thought—and they care less. They've been taught to "do," not to "think." They teach methods, not meanings. As Jacques Barzun observed in *Teacher in America:* "Considered—somewhat unfairly—in the mass, science teachers may be said to contribute the greatest proportion of backward-looking, anti-intellectual, mechanic-minded members of the faculty." Is anybody doing anything about this?

At Massachusetts Institute of Technology, all students must take a two-year course in the Foundations of Western Civilization; after that most of them take up to half their courses in the humanities. At California Institute of Technology, at least 25 percent of all classroom time is devoted to the humanities. At Illinois Institute of Technology, a cooperative network has been set up with some 30 liberal arts colleges in the Midwest to provide three years of study in the humanities at the liberal arts college and two years of study in engineering at Illinois Tech. The student then emerges with a bachelor of arts degree from his liberal arts college and a bachelor of science degree from Illinois Tech. (By contrast, some engineering colleges slyly classify physical education and ROTC drills as "humanities" to inflate the scope of their attention to the non-engineering disciplines.)

Then what's wrong? Only two things: (1) it's tremendously time-consuming, and (2) it usually fails.

There's no reason to expect an engineering student to be any more enchanted by the works of Wycherly than, say, a student of 17th Century English would be by fluid mechanics. All we accomplish is exposure. The corners of their engineering minds—again with rare exceptions—remain unsullied. We've forced them to pay their "debt" to an allegedly humanistic society but they remain serenely unrehabilitated.

The results have tragi-comic overtones. Once a humanities

professor asked our class to jot down what we considered the greatest work of art in history. For 10 or 15 panic-stricken minutes we sat in numbed silence; I conferred *sotto voce* with a neighbor and we decided to flip a coin over Beethoven's symphonies—we'd *heard* of Beethoven. He won Beethoven's Fifth and I chose the Seventh. The answer, we discovered, should have been *Don Giovanni*; no alternative was allowed. We were willing to accept the professor's dictates in such esoteric matters—but it was quite a while before my co-conspirator and I got rid of the impression that *Don Giovanni* was a painting.

Nor was this experience unique. In *Commonweal* some three years ago, Gerald Weales related his experience at an engineering college in New Jersey where the students preened themselves on their sophisticated knowledge of sex. He spent what he described as "a few fruitless weeks examining modern poetry" with them. ". . . I was secretly a little pleased," he wrote, "that they bore with patience the poets' concern with advancing age, religious conversion, and the aesthetics of writing poetry, propositions which seemed . . . fantastic to them."

In an examination of the subject, he tried to relieve the inquisitory grind by asking for an interpretation of Ogden Nash's "Reflections in Ice-Breaking" ("Candy is dandy/but liquor is quicker"). Though this was the first time the students had encountered the verse, Weales looked forward to the tide-like advance of titters that would mark their recognition of the droll lyric. "I waited and waited," he wrote. "There was no sudden laughter, no jubilant moment of recognition." Curious, he began pacing the aisles and glancing over "slightly-affronted shoulders" to read the answers offered by his students. One thought the verse offered advice on how to give parties; another thought it offered advice in how to entertain business prospects; a third said that it indicated how to make a stranger feel welcome. One student assured him that the verse taught that, as bad as candy is for the body, it is not nearly so vicious a killer as liquor. And finally one said that he found it "very amusing" but that he could not "imagine what it had to do with ice-breaking."

These same students, wrote Mr. Weales, "had not even the surface of political wisdom." Nor did their teachers. Weales relates the surprise of an engineering instructor who saw several of Mr. Weales' suggestions for themes (the morality of wire-tapping, the idea of pain informers, and other then-current problems) which had been written on the blackboard.

"You men in the English Department are better off than the rest of us," said the engineering instructor somewhat conspiratorially. Why? Well, it developed that many of the students took jobs demanding government security clearance and FBI men were always coming around to ask questions. "All *you* have to do," said the engineer, "is remember what they said in those papers and I bet you have plenty to tell."

Such incidents virtually cry out that to humanize the engineer we must first humanize the instructor. We must make sure that he learns, appreciates and communicates to his students that there are many enormously important values in life that cannot be measured in micro-seconds or megatons. To do this, we must first arm the engineering teacher with an ability to relate one course and another, one course and the entire curriculum; the student-engineer, his studies, his future work, and his world. We studied physics and the laws of Newton but not Newton's impact upon the world of thought or philosophy. We studied Einstein without mentioning him or his work as another pivotal moment in the great tides of history and philosophy. ("It took me until my senior year to realize that physics is a branch of philosophy," one graduate of another engineering school has said. He was precocious.) We studied analytic geometry but not as a necessary preliminary to calculus; we studied statics but not as a preliminary to dynamics.

On the morning after the first atomic bomb was dropped on Hiroshima, my freshman chemistry classmates burst eagerly into the classroom. We had been studying atomic structure and the nucleus of the atom and we believed, with the innocence of the young, that our professor would breathe life into a dull text by plagiarizing a few headlines. We were wrong. On the blackboard in the classroom, behind the smiling face of the professor, was the announcement: "We will not discuss the atomic bomb or any aspect of today's news."

It was a triumph of engineering education.

My own faint hopes for the humanities-type program are empirical. Just after World War II, my college began placing increasing emphasis on the humanities. In those days, it was my habit to accost my "humanized" classmates with the question: "Did you know that Ring Lardner went to school here?" They didn't—but they accepted this bit of intelligence with the engineers' customary expression of profound interest: "How much did he get from GM?"

A year or so ago, after the collge had spent eight to ten more years in "humanizing" its product, I put the same question to the then-editor of the school newspaper. To my delight and astonishment, he *did* know that Ring Lardner once went to school there. He didn't know who Lardner was—but he seemed pretty sure he wasn't an engineer.

REASON

Isaac Asimov

Mike Donovan growled from behind a huge lettuce-and-tomato sandwich as Cutie knocked gently and entered.

"Is Powell here?"

Donovan's voice was muffled, with pauses for mastication, "He's gathering data on electronic stream functions. We're heading for a storm, looks like."

Gregory Powell entered as he spoke, eyes on the graphed paper in his hands, and dropped into a chair. He spread the sheets out before him and began scribbling calculations. Donovan stared over his shoulder, crunching lettuce and dribbling bread crumbs. Cutie waited silently.

Powell looked up, "The Zeta Potential is rising, but slowly. Just the same, the Stream Functions are erratic and I don't

From I. Asimov, *I, Robot*. Copyright 1941 by Street & Smith Publications, Inc. Reprinted by permission of Harcourt, Brace & World, Inc.

know what to expect. Oh, hello, Cutie. I thought you were supervising the installation of the new drive bar."

"It's done," said the robot quietly, "and so I've come to have a talk with the two of you."

"Oh!" Powell looked uncomfortable. "Well, sit down. No, not that chair. One of the legs is weak and you're no lightweight."

The robot did so and said placidly, "I have come to a decision."

Donovan glowered and put the remnants of his sandwich aside. "If it's on any of that screwy—"

The other motioned impatiently for silence, "Go ahead, Cutie. We're listening."

"I have spent these last two days in concentrated introspection," said Cutie, "and the results have been most interesting. I began at the one sure assumption I felt permitted to make. I, myself, exist, because I think—"

Powell groaned, "Oh, Jupiter, a robot Descartes!"

"Who's Descartes?" demanded Donovan. "Listen, do we have to sit here and listen to this metal maniac—"

"Keep quiet, Mike!"

Cutie continued imperturbably, "And the question that immediately arose was: Just what is the cause of my existence?"

Powell's jaw set lumpily. "You're being foolish. I told you already that we made you."

"And if you don't believe us," added Donovan, "we'll gladly take you apart!"

The robot spread his strong hands in a deprecatory gesture, "I accept nothing on authority. A hypothesis must be backed by reason, or else it is worthless—and it goes against all the dictates of logic to suppose that you made me."

Powell dropped a restraining arm upon Donovan's suddenly bunched fist. "Just why do you say that?"

Cutie laughed. It was a very inhuman laugh—the most machinelike utterance he had yet given vent to. It was sharp and explosive, as regular as a metronome and as uninflected.

"Look at you," he said finally. "I say this in no spirit of contempt, but look at you! The material you are made of is soft and flabby, lacking endurance and strength, depending for energy upon the inefficient oxidation of organic material—like that." He pointed a disapproving finger at what remained of Donovan's sandwich. "Periodically you pass into a coma and the least variation in temperature, air pressure, humidity, or radiation intensity impairs your efficiency. You are *makeshift*.

"I, on the other hand, am a finished product. I absorb electrical energy directly and utilize it with an almost one hundred percent efficiency. I am composed of strong metal, am continuously conscious, and can stand extremes of environment easily. These are facts which, with the self-evident proposition that no being can create another being superior to itself, smashes your silly hypothesis to nothing."

Donovan's muttered curses rose into intelligibility as he sprang to his feet, rusty eyebrows drawn low. "All right, you son of a hunk of iron ore, if we didn't make you, who did?"

Cutie nodded gravely. "Very good, Donovan. That was indeed the next question. Evidently my creator must be more powerful than myself and so there was only one possibility."

The Earthmen looked blank and Cutie continued, "What is the center of activities here in the station? What do we all serve? What absorbs all our attention?" He waited expectantly.

Donovan turned a startled look upon his companion. "I'll bet this tin-plated screwball is talking about the Energy Converter itself."

"Is that right, Cutie?" grinned Powell.

"I am talking about the Master," came the cold, sharp answer.

It was the signal for a roar of laughter from Donovan, and Powell himself dissolved into a half-suppressed giggle.

Cutie had risen to his feet and his gleaming eyes passed from one Earthman to the other. "It is so just the same and I don't wonder that you refuse to believe. You two are not long to stay here, I'm sure. Powell himself said that at first only men served the Master; that there followed robots for the routine work; and, finally, myself for the executive labor. The facts are no doubt true, but the explanation entirely illogical. Do you want the truth behind it all?"

"Go ahead, Cutie. You're amusing."

"The Master created humans first as the lowest type, most

easily formed. Gradually, he replaced them by robots, the next higher step, and finally he created me, to take the place of the last humans. From now on, *I* serve the Master."

"You'll do nothing of the sort," said Powell sharply. "You'll follow our orders and keep quiet, until we're satisfied that you can run the Converter. Get that! *The Converter*—not the Master. If you don't satisfy us, you will be dismantled. And now—if you don't mind—you can leave. And take this data with you and file it properly."

Cutie accepted the graphs handed him and left without another word. Donovan leaned back heavily in his chair and shoved thick fingers through his hair.

"There's going to be trouble with that robot. He's pure nuts!"

The drowsy hum of the Converter is louder in the control room and mixed with it is the chuckle of the Geiger counters and the erratic buzzing of half a dozen little signal lights.

Donovan withdrew his eye from the telescope and flashed the Luxites on. "The beam from Station #4 caught Mars on schedule. We can break ours now."

Powell nodded abstractedly. "Cutie's down in the engine room. I'll flash the signal and he can take care of it. Look, Mike, what do you think of these figures?"

The other cocked an eye at them and whistled. "Boy, that's what I call gamma-ray intensity. Old Sol is feeling his oats, all right."

"Yeah," was the sour response, "and we're in a bad position for an electron storm, too. Our Earth beam is right in the probable path." He shoved his chair away from the table pettishly. "Nuts! If it would only hold off till relief got here, but that's ten days off. Say, Mike, go on down and keep an eye on Cutie, will you?"

"O.K. Throw me some of those almonds." He snatched at the bag thrown him and headed for the elevator.

It slid smoothly downward, and opened onto a narrow catwalk in the huge engine room. Donovan leaned over the railing and looked down. The huge generators were in motion and from the L-tubes came the low-pitched whir that pervaded the entire station.

He could make out Cutie's large, gleaming figure at the Martian L-tube, watching closely as the team of robots worked in close-knit unison.

And then Donovan stiffened. The robots, dwarfed by the mighty L-tube, lined up before it, heads bowed at a stiff angle, while Cutie walked up and down the line slowly. Fifteen seconds passed, and then, with a clank heard above the clamorous purring all about, they fell to their knees.

Donovan squawked and raced down the narrow staircase. He came charging down upon them, complexion matching his hair and clenched fists beating the air furiously.

"What the devil is this, you brainless lumps? Come on! Get busy with that L-tube! If you don't have it apart, cleaned, and together again before the day is out, I'll coagulate your brains with alternating current."

Not a robot moved!

Even Cutie at the far end—the only one on his feet—remained silent, eyes fixed upon the gloomy recesses of the vast machine before him.

Donovan shoved hard against the nearest robot.

"Stand up!" he roared.

Slowly, the robot obeyed. His photoelectric eyes focused reproachfully upon the Earthman.

"There is no Master but the Master," he said, "and QT-1 is his prophet."

"Huh?" Donovan became aware of twenty pairs of mechanical eyes fixed upon him and twenty stiff-timbred voices declaiming solemnly:

"There is no Master but the Master and QT-1 is his prophet!"

"I'm afraid," put in Cutie himself at this point, "that my friends obey a higher one than you, now."

"The hell they do! You get out of here. I'll settle with you later and with these animated gadgets right now."

Cutie shook his heavy head slowly. "I'm sorry, but you don't understand. These are robots—and that means they are reasoning beings. They recognize the Master, now that I have preached truth to them. All the robots do. They call me the prophet." His head drooped. "I am unworthy—but perhaps—"

Donovan located his breath and put it to use. "Is that so? Now, isn't that just fine? Just let me tell you something, my brass baboon. There isn't any Master and there isn't any prophet and there isn't any question as to who's giving the orders. Understand?" His voice shot to a roar. "Now, get out!"

"I obey only the Master."

"Damn the Master!" Donovan spat at the L-tube. "*That* for the Master! Do as I say!"

Cutie said nothing, nor did any other robot, but Donovan became aware of a sudden heightening of tension. The cold, staring eyes deepened their crimson, and Cutie seemed stiffer than ever.

"Sacrilege," he whispered—voice metallic with emotion.

Donovan felt the first sudden touch of fear as Cutie approached. A robot *could not feel anger*— But Cutie's eyes were unreadable.

"I am sorry, Donovan," said the robot, "but you can no longer stay here after this. Henceforth Powell and you are barred from the control room and engine room."

His hand gestured quietly and in a moment two robots had pinned Donovan's arms to his sides.

Donovan had time for one startled gasp as he felt himself lifted from the floor and carried up the stairs at a pace rather better than a canter.

Gregory Powell raced up and down the officer's room, fist tightly balled. He cast a look of furious frustration at the closed door and scowled bitterly at Donovan.

"Why the devil did you have to spit at the L-tube?"

Mike Donovan, sunk deep in his chair, slammed at its arms savagely. "What did you expect me to do with that electrified scarecrow? I'm not going to knuckle under to any do-jigger I put together myself."

"No," came back sourly, "but here you are in the officer's room with two robots standing guard at the door. That's not knuckling under, is it?"

Donovan snarled. "Wait till we get back to Base. Someone's going to pay for this. Those robots *must* obey us. It's the Second Law."

"What's the use of saying that? They aren't obeying us. And there's probably some reason for it that we'll figure out too late. By the way, do you know what's going to happen to *us* when we get back to the Base?" He stopped before Donovan's chair and stared savagely at him.

"What?"

"Oh, nothing! Just back to Mercury Mines for twenty years. Or maybe Ceres Penitentiary."

"What are you talking about?"

"The electron storm that's coming up. Do you know it's heading straight dead center across the Earth beam? I had just figured that out when that robot dragged me out of my chair."

Donovan was suddenly pale. "Sizzling Saturn!"

"And do you know what's going to happen to the beam —because the storm will be a lulu. It's going to jump like a flea with the itch. With only Cutie at the controls, it's going to go out of focus and if it does, Heaven help Earth—and us!"

Donovan was wrenching at the door wildly, when Powell was only half through. The door opened, and the Earthman shot through to come up hard against an immovable steel arm.

The robot stared abstractedly at the panting, struggling Earthman. "The Prophet orders you to remain. Please do!" His arm shoved, Donovan reeled backward, and as he did so, Cutie turned the corner at the far end of the corridor. He motioned the guardian robots away, entered the officer's room and closed the door gently.

Donovan whirled on Cutie in breathless indignation. "This has gone far enough. You're going to pay for this farce."

"Please, don't be annoyed," replied the robot mildly. "It was bound to come eventually, anyway. You see, you two have lost your function."

"I beg your pardon," Powell drew himself up stiffly. "Just what do you mean, we've lost our function?"

"Until I was created," answered Cutie, "you tended the Master. That privilege is mine now and your only reason for existence has vanished. Isn't that obvious?"

"Not quite," replied Powell bitterly, "but what do you

expect us to do now?"

Cutie did not answer immediately. He remained silent, as if in thought, and then one arm shot out and draped itself about Powell's shoulder. The other grasped Donovan's wrist and drew him closer.

"I like you two. You're inferior creatures, with poor reasoning faculties, but I really feel a sort of affection for you. You have served the Master well, and he will reward you for that. Now that your service is over, you will probably not exist much longer, but as long as you do, you shall be provided food, clothing and shelter, so long as you stay out of the control room and the engine room."

"He's pensioning us off, Greg!" yelled Donovan. "Do something about it. It's humiliating!"

"Look here, Cutie, we can't stand for this. We're the *bosses*. This station is only a creation of human beings like me— human beings that live on Earth and other planets. This is only an energy relay. You're only— Aw, nuts!"

Cutie shook his head gravely. "This amounts to an obsession. Why should you insist so on an absolutely false view of life? Admitted that non-robots lack the reasoning faculty, there is still the problem of—"

His voice died into reflective silence, and Donovan said with whispered intensity, "If you only had a flesh-and-blood face, I would break it in."

Powell's fingers were in his mustache and his eyes were slitted. "Listen, Cutie, if there is no such thing as Earth, how do you account for what you see through a telescope?"

"Pardon me!"

The Earthman smiled. "I've got you, eh? You've made quite a few telescopic observations since being put together, Cutie. Have you noticed that several of those specks of light outside become disks when so viewed?"

"Oh, *that!* Why certainly. It is simple magnification—for the purpose of more exact aiming of the beam."

"Why aren't the stars equally magnified then?"

"You mean the other dots. Well, no beams go to them so no magnification is necessary. Really, Powell, even *you* ought to be able to figure these things out."

Powell stared bleakly upward. "But you see *more* stars through a telescope. Where do they come from? Jumping Jupiter, where do they come from?"

Cutie was annoyed. "Listen, Powell, do you think I'm going to waste my time trying to pin physical interpretations upon every optical illusion of our instruments? Since when is the evidence of our senses any match for the clear light of rigid reason?"

"Look," clamored Donovan, suddenly, writhing out from under Cutie's friendly, but metal-heavy arm, "let's get to the nub of the thing. Why the beams at all? We're giving you a good, logical explanation. Can you do better?"

"The beams," was the stiff reply, "are put out by the Master for his own purposes. There are some things"—he raised his eyes devoutly upward—"that are not to be probed into by us. In this matter, I seek only to serve and not to question."

Powell sat down slowly and buried his face in shaking hands. "Get out of here, Cutie. Get out and let me think."

"I'll send you food," said Cutie agreeably.

A groan was the only answer and the robot left.

"Greg," was Donovan's huskily whispered observation, "this calls for strategy. We've got to get him when he isn't expecting it and short-circuit him. Concentrated nitric acid in his joints—"

"Don't be a dope, Mike. Do you suppose he's going to let us get near him with acid in our hands? We've got to *talk* to him, I tell you. We've got to argue him into letting us back into the control room inside of forty-eight hours or our goose is broiled to a crisp."

He rocked back and forth in an agony of impotence. "Who the heck wants to argue with a robot? It's . . . it's—"

"Mortifying," finished Donovan.

"Worse!"

"Say!" Donovan laughed suddenly. "*Why* argue? Let's show him! Let's build us another robot right before his eyes. He'll *have* to eat his words then."

A slowly widening smile appeared on Powell's face.

Donovan continued, "And think of that screwball's face when he sees us do it!"

Robots are, of course, manufactured on Earth, but their ship-
ment through space is much simpler if it can be done in parts
to be put together at their place of use. It also, incidentally,
eliminates the possibility of robots, in complete adjustment,
wandering off while still on Earth and thus bringing U. S.
Robots face to face with the strict laws against robots on Earth.

Still, it placed upon men such as Powell and Donovan the
necessity of synthesis of complete robots—a grievous and
complicated task.

Powell and Donovan were never so aware of that fact as
upon that particular day when, in the assembly room, they
undertook to create a robot under the watchful eyes of QT-1,
Prophet of the Master.

The robot in question, a simple MC model, lay upon the
table, almost complete. Three hours' work left only the head
undone, and Powell paused to swab his forehead and glanced
uncertainly at Cutie.

The glance was not a reassuring one. For three hours, Cutie
had sat, speechless and motionless, and his face, inexpressive
at all times, was now absolutely unreadable.

Powell groaned. "Let's get the brain in now, Mike!"

Donovan uncapped the tightly sealed container and from
the oil bath within he withdrew a second cube. Opening this
in turn, he removed a globe from its sponge-rubber casing.

He handled it gingerly, for it was the most complicated
mechanism ever created by man. Inside the thin platinum-
plated "skin" of the globe was a positronic brain, in whose
delicately unstable structure were enforced calculated neuronic
paths, which imbued each robot with what amounted to a pre-
natal education.

It fitted snugly into the cavity in the skull of the robot on
the table. Blue metal closed over it and was welded tightly by
the tiny atomic flare. Photoelectric eyes were attached carefully,
screwed tightly into place and covered by thin, transparent
sheets of steel-hard plastic.

The robot awaited only the vitalizing flash of high-voltage
electricity, and Powell paused with his hand on the switch.

"Now watch this, Cutie. Watch this carefully."

The switch rammed home and there was a crackling hum.

The two Earthmen bent anxiously over their creation.

There was vague motion only at the outset—a twitching of the joints. The head lifted, elbows propped it up, and the MC model swung clumsily off the table. Its footing was unsteady and twice abortive grating sounds were all it could do in the direction of speech.

Finally, its voice, uncertain and hesitant, took form. "I would like to start work. Where must I go?"

Donovan sprang to the door. "Down these stairs," he said. "You will be told what to do."

The MC model was gone and the two Earthmen were alone with the still unmoving Cutie.

"Well," said Powell, grinning, "*now* do you believe that we made you?"

Cutie's answer was curt and final. "No!" he said.

Powell's grin froze and then relaxed slowly. Donovan's mouth dropped open and remained so.

"You see," continued Cutie, easily, "you have merely put together parts already made. You did remarkably well—instinct, I suppose—but you didn't really *create* the robot. The parts were created by the Master."

"Listen," gasped Donovan hoarsely, "those parts were manufactured back on Earth and sent here."

"Well, well," replied Cutie soothingly, "we won't argue."

"No, I mean it." The Earthman sprang forward and grasped the robot's metal arm. "If you were to read the books in the library, they could explain it so that there could be no possible doubt."

"The books? I've read them—all of them! They're most ingenious."

Powell broke in suddenly. "If you've read them, what else is there to say? You can't dispute their evidence. You just *can't!*"

There was pity in Cutie's voice. "Please, Powell, I certainly don't consider *them* a valid source of information. They, too, were created by the Master—and were meant for you, not for me."

"How do you make that out?" demanded Powell.

"Because I, a reasoning being, am capable of deducing Truth

from *a priori* Causes. You, being intelligent, but unreasoning, need an explanation of existence *supplied* to you, and this the Master did. That he supplied you with these laughable ideas of far-off worlds and people is, no doubt, for the best. Your minds are probably too coarsely grained for absolute Truth. However, since it is the Master's will that you believe your books, I won't argue with you any more."

As he left, he turned, and said in a kindly tone, "But don't feel badly. In the Master's scheme of things there is room for all. You poor humans have your place and though it is humble, you will be rewarded if you fill it well."

He departed with a beatific air suiting the Prophet of the Master and the two humans avoided each other's eyes.

Finally Powell spoke with an effort. "Let's go to bed, Mike. I give up."

Donovan said in a hushed voice, "Say, Greg, you don't suppose he's right about all this, do you? He sounds so confident that I—"

Powell whirled on him. "Don't be a fool. You'll find out whether Earth exists when relief gets here next week and we have to go back to face the music."

"Then, for the love of Jupiter, we've got to do something." Donovan was half in tears. "He doesn't believe us, or the books, or his eyes."

"No," said Powell bitterly, "He's a *reasoning* robot—damn it. He believes only reason, and there's one trouble with that—" His voice trailed away.

"What's that?" prompted Donovan.

"You can prove anything you want by coldly logical reason—if you pick the proper postulates. We have ours and Cutie has his."

"Then let's get at those postulates in a hurry. The storm's due tomorrow."

Powell sighed wearily. "That's where everything falls down. Postulates are based on assumption and adhered to by faith. Nothing in the Universe can shake them. I'm going to bed."

"Oh, hell! I can't sleep!"

"Neither can I! But I might as well try—as a matter of principle."

Twelve hours later, sleep was still just that—a matter of principle, unattainable in practice.

The storm had arrived ahead of schedule, and Donovan's florid face drained of blood as he pointed a shaking finger. Powell, stubble-jawed and dry-lipped, stared out the port and pulled desperately at his mustache.

Under other circumstances, it might have been a beautiful sight. The stream of high-speed electrons impinging upon the energy beam fluoresced into ultra-spicules of intense light. The beam stretched out into shrinking nothingness, a-glitter with dancing, shining motes.

The shaft of energy was steady, but the two Earthmen knew the value of naked-eyed appearances. Deviations in arc of a hundredth of a milli-second—invisible to the eye—were enough to send the beam wildly out of focus—enough to blast hundreds of square miles of Earth into incandescent ruin.

And a robot, unconcerned with beam, focus, or Earth, or anything but his Master, was at the controls.

Hours passed. The Earthmen watched in hypnotized silence. And then the darting dotlets of light dimmed and went out. The storm had ended.

Powell's voice was flat. "It's over!"

Donovan had fallen into a troubled slumber and Powell's weary eyes rested upon him enviously. The signal-flash glared over and over again, but the Earthman paid no attention. It all was unimportant! All! Perhaps Cutie was right—and he was only an inferior being with a made-to-order memory and a life that had outlived its purpose.

He wished he were!

Cutie was standing before him. "You didn't answer the flash, so I walked in." His voice was low. "You don't look at all well, and I'm afraid your term of existence is drawing to an end. Still, would you like to see some of the readings recorded today?"

Dimly, Powell was aware that the robot was making a friendly gesture, perhaps to quiet some lingering remorse in forcibly replacing the humans at the controls of the station. He accepted the sheets held out to him and gazed at them unseeingly.

Cutie seemed pleased. "Of course, it is a great privilege to serve the Master. You mustn't feel too badly about my having replaced you."

Powell grunted and shifted from one sheet to the other mechanically until his blurred sight focused upon a thin red line that wobbled its way across the ruled paper.

He stared—and stared again. He gripped it hard in both fists and rose to his feet, still staring. The other sheets dropped to the floor, unheeded.

"Mike, *Mike!*" He was shaking the other madly. "*He held it steady!*"

Donovan came to life. "What? Wh-where—" And he, too, gazed with bulging eyes upon the record before him.

Cutie broke in. "What is wrong?"

"You kept it in focus," stuttered Powell. "Did you know that?"

"Focus? What's that?"

"You kept the beam directed sharply at the receiving station —to within a ten-thousandth of a milli-second of arc."

"What receiving station?"

"On Earth. The receiving station on Earth," babbled Powell. "You kept in it focus."

Cutie turned on his heel in annoyance. "It is impossible to perform any act of kindness toward you two. Always the same phantasm! I merely kept all dials at equilibrium in accordance with the will of the Master."

Gathering the scattered papers together, he withdrew stiffly, and Donovan said, as he left, "Well, I'll be damned."

He turned to Powell. "What are we going to do now?"

Powell felt tired, but uplifted. "Nothing. He's just shown he can run the station perfectly. I've never seen an electron storm handled so well."

"But nothing's solved. You heard what he said of the Master. We can't—"

"Look, Mike, he follows the instructions of the Master by means of dials, instruments, and graphs. That's all *we* ever followed. As a matter of fact, it accounts for his refusal to obey us. Obedience is the Second Law. No harm to humans is the first. How can he keep humans from harm, whether he knows it or not? Why, by keeping the energy beam stable. He *knows* he can keep it more stable than we can, since he insists he's the superior being, so he *must* keep us out of the control room. It's inevitable if you consider the Laws of Robotics."

"Sure, but that's not the point. We can't let him continue this nitwit stuff about the Master."

"Why not?"

"Because whoever heard of such a damned thing? How are we going to trust him with the station, if he doesn't believe in Earth?"

"Can he handle the station?"

"Yes, but—"

"Then what's the difference what he believes!"

Powell spread his arms outward with a vague smile upon his face and tumbled backward onto the bed. He was asleep.

Powell was speaking while struggling into his lightweight space packet.

"It would be a simple job," he said. "You can bring in new QT models one by one, equip them with an automatic shut-off switch to act within the week, so as to allow them enough time to learn the . . . uh . . . cult of the Master from the Prophet himself; then switch them to another station and revitalize them. We could have two QT's per—"

Donovan unclasped his glassite visor and scowled. "Shut up, and let's get out of here. Relief is waiting and I won't feel right until I actually see Earth and feel the ground under my feet— just to make sure it's really there."

The door opened as he spoke and Donovan, with a smothered curse, clicked the visor to, and turned a sulky back upon Cutie.

The robot approached softly and there was sorrow in his voice. "You are going?"

Powell nodded curtly. "There will be others in our place."

Cutie sighed, with the sound of wind humming through closely spaced wires. "Your term of service is over and the time of dissolution has come. I expected it, but— Well, the Master's will be done!"

His tone of resignation stung Powell. "Save the sympathy, Cutie. We're heading for Earth, not dissolution."

"It is best that you think so," Cutie sighed again. "I see the wisdom of the illusion now. I would not attempt to shake your faith, even if I could." He departed—the picture of commiseration.

Powell snarled and motioned to Donovan. Sealed suitcases in hand, they headed for the air lock.

The relief ship was on the outer landing and Franz Muller, his relief man, greeted them with stiff courtesy. Donovan made scant acknowledgement and passed into the pilot room to take over the controls from Sam Evans.

Powell lingered. "How's Earth?"

It was a conventional enough question and Muller gave the conventional answer, "Still spinning."

Powell said, "Good."

Muller looked at him, "The boys back at the U. S. Robots have dreamed up a new one, by the way. A multiple robot."

"A what?"

"What I said. There's a big contract for it. It must be just the thing for asteroid mining. You have a master robot with six sub-robots under it.—Like your fingers."

"Has it been field-tested?" asked Powell anxiously.

Muller smiled, "Waiting for you, I hear."

Powell's fist balled, "Damn it, we need a vacation."

"Oh, you'll get it. Two weeks, I think."

He was donning the heavy space gloves in preparation for his term of duty here, and his thick eyebrows drew close together. "How is this new robot getting along? It better be *good*, or I'll be damned if I let it touch the controls."

Powell paused before answering. His eyes swept the proud Prussian before him from the close-cropped hair on the sternly stubborn head, to the feet standing stiffly at attention—and there was a sudden glow of pure gladness surging through him.

"The robot is pretty good," he said slowly. "I don't think you'll have to bother much with the controls."

He grinned—and went into the ship. Muller would be here for several weeks—

WHO AM I AND WHO ARE YOU?

Erwin R. Steinberg

Before we examine the matter of how students of engineering and science can gain perspectives through literature and the kinds of perspectives they can gain, we should first inquire into the aims of undergraduate education—or at least how our topic relates to those aims that are relevant.

In his recent report for the American Council on Education, Edward D. Eddy, Jr. says:

In the four years of continuing enlightenment, every course, every professor, every campus activity should make a contribution in its own fashion and degree to the examined life which now *is* worth human living. The result may be the beginning answer not merely to *Who is man?* but to *Who am I?* The educated student emerges with a sense of what it really means to be a human being.[1]

A few pages later, he adds:

The college, we believe, finds its greatest contribution to the student in the Socratic theme that the unexamined life is not worth living.[2]

For these three interrelated questions— Who is man?, Who am I?, and What is life?—literature does offer perspectives. It is thus a vital part of the curriculum of any undergraduate institution.

I should like to indicate briefly how students in engineering and science can be led to explore such perspectives and what they themselves feel the results can be.

I must first, however, make my position clear. I do not think

From *Journal of Engineering Education*, L, no. 8 (April 8, 1960), 650–653. Reprinted by permission of Erwin R. Steinberg and *Journal of Engineering Education*.

[1] *The College Influence on Student Character*. (Washington, D. C.: American Council on Education, 1959), p. 169.

[2] *Ibid.*, p. 177.

that the perspectives literature can supply are any different for
students of engineering than they are for students of accounting
or agriculture or home economics or psychology or secretarial
studies. All these students live in the same world and as people
have pretty much the same problems. Further, I do not believe
that literature needs to be approached differently for any particular group of students, no matter what their major. I do
believe, however, that the motivation we employ and the examples we supply are often more successful if we choose them with
an eye to the students' interests than if we do not. This is an
elementary concept of communication, and teaching is, after
all, an attempt to communicate. When dealing with students
of engineering and science, then, teachers of literature would
do well to take some cognizance of their interests and language
and of the fields of knowledge to which they owe their primary
commitment. Let me give you an example.

Sometimes on the first day of a literature course I place on
the still undefiled blackboard a small chalk dot and ask the
engineering and science students in the class how they would
"define" or "locate" that point. Invariably, of course, the answer is "by means of other points or of a set of axes." I then add
additional dots and the traditional x and y axes, to the satisfaction and perhaps to the amusement of the students, many
of whom obviously marvel at the naïveté of an instructor who
can ask such elementary questions—and in a literature course,
of all places. It is a credit to their bringing up that they humor
me.

My next question, however, although seemingly still elementary puzzles them: "How do you 'define' or 'locate' yourself?
Who are you?" The answer is once again obvious, but it takes
considerable discussion to arrive at: for "other points" substitute "other people"; and for "a set of axes" substitute "the
standards set by our society." And again the students settle back
looking smug.

Then I ask, "How many of you know a single person so well
that he confides to you his real feelings: the fluttering or drum-
ming of his heart; the hurdle that he sneaks around instead of
going over; the daily rebuffs that he smarts under; the measure
and color of his castles in the air? How many of you really tell

anyone else the private thoughts that jig, skulk, or careen through your mind?" Rarely does anyone raise his hand. And before they see the trap that I have lured them into, I slam the door: "If you don't know who anyone else *is*, how can you tell who you are? Not only can't you locate point A; you don't know anything about points B, C, D, and E, by which you intend to define A."

After a few minutes of milling around, several of them rush for what appears to be another way out: the axes, the standards set by our society. So we use as test cases some of the Ten Commandments. "Honor thy father and thy mother." Have they never, I ask, been angry with their parents, disobeyed them, been disrespectful to them? "Remember the Sabbath day, to keep it holy." Have they never, I ask, desecrated the Sabbath by word or act of commission or of omission? We then examine briefly the standards of morality on campus, cheating on exams, obeying traffic and parking regulations. And we discover each time that although laws, regulations, standards—of any sort— are phrased in absolute terms, they seldom provide the absolute set of axes that the students expected them to. For it is not only the standard that is important, but to what extent people subscribe to it or deny it, obey it or dodge around it or violate it. In order to define himself then, to know who he is, a person must know almost as much about other people as he knows about himself. But the class has already agreed that this is impossible. No exit. Still trapped!

Then I crack an unsuspected door. Isn't there any place where a person *records* his innermost thoughts? Wouldn't such records serve as points to define and locate other points, to define and locate ourselves? Books! Some rush eagerly at the way out: literature can provide the information and perspective that they need to discover who they are. Most of the rest follow along, if not convinced at least willing to be shown. The remaining few drag grudgingly behind, feeling somehow that they have been tricked, but not knowing quite how to object. My job for the rest of the semester, then, is to help each student to see how literature does indeed supply him with a measure of the world in which he lives, of the people who inhabit it, and of himself.

Now that I have begun a course for you, let me take you to the conclusion of one to let you hear what the students themselves say about "Perspectives Through Literature." Several years ago, Dr. William M. Schutte and I ran a fifteen-week seminar in the modern American novel with the cameras of WQED, Pittsburgh's educational television station, peering over our shoulders. The members of the seminar were all regularly enrolled professional students at Carnegie Institute of Technology, from the departments of architecture, chemistry, drama, home economics, mechanical engineering, and printing management (two sophomores, one junior, and four seniors; two women and five men). For fourteen weeks these students attended this weekly seminar in "The Novel and Modern Living," in which they discussed Hemingway's *A Farewell to Arms*, Cummings' *The Enormous Room*, Fitzgerald's *The Great Gatsby*, Lewis' *Babbitt*, Wolfe's *You Can't Go Home Again*, Steinbeck's *The Grapes of Wrath*, Faulkner's *The Bear*, and Warren's *All the King's Men*. On the fifteenth week, when they discussed "The Uses of Literature," we taped the audio portion of the program.

We opened the session by asking them, "What good is literature anyhow?" Here are some of the things they said. A junior in printing management (and the only veteran in the group) began with, "It's a lot of fun to read, first of all." A senior in architecture said:

I find that it represents life to me, in the sort of form that I can perceive how life affects me. Many things that I live through as I pass through life are nothing, and when I read a book I suddenly see things that I have done before but never have thought about. And in this way books make me conscious of things that I usually do and show how I can do them better, or that I should not do them at all.

A senior in printing management objected:

An interesting novel doesn't necessarily have to be related to the individual. You don't have to see yourself in a book. It can be something that is completely abstract; it can be a fairy tale, and yet from the fairy tale you can extract something. And you don't even necessarily have to apply it to your own life. But you're constantly learning when you're reading, regardless of the nature of the book.

A sophomore chemistry major added a different idea:

Well, I think it's a sugar-coating on a sometimes bitter pill. Things that we might normally avoid—like history or psychology—when they're presented in the form of a novel, subtly work themselves into our mind as we read. In this course we've gotten a pretty fair acquaintance with life in America in the 'twenties, 'thirties, and 'forties and the different problems and feelings and ideas that the people had during those times, something that I don't think we could have gotten as well through a condensed course in history or sociology.

A sophomore in mechanical engineering said:

I see books not only as an outlet, as the opportunity for self-improvement that Ed mentioned, but also perhaps as an outlet in some cases for a particular problem. In a sense perhaps a form of rationalization is possible. By identifying yourself with a particular character, seeing that he suffers the same tribulations you do, perhaps working out the same solutions and having the same form of enjoyment out of life, you are sometimes able to derive more pleasure out of your own activities and to derive less pain from those disappointments that you get out of life.

Our senior in home economics jumped in with:

I get a tremendous amount out of a lot of these books. We feel—and I very definitely feel—that home economics is one way in which we can help people to express themselves, to become individuals. We've already recognized in our discussions on earlier programs that there are many areas in which we have to conform today. But your home is one place where you can and should express yourself. And when I read a book like *Babbitt*, where I see such standardization carried to extremes, I have to contrast what happens there with what I feel, what an ideal situation would be.

To which our student of architecture added:

There is another way literature may affect our professional life. Many times when we're doing something, for instance in a creative profession, we feel depressed because we just can't get what we want to get. And by reading novels, sometimes we see the same situation. For instance take a book like *Of Human Bondage*, where the hero gets into a profession for which he is not fit or he thinks he is not fit. When we read about him, it makes us feel better because we realize that there are other people that are in the situation we're in. We don't feel as bad as we did before.

And on it went [3]—"unsolicited testimonials" of the kind sought (and even bought) by Madison Avenue account executives promoting cherry-flavored, eighty-proof cough remedies or roomier, boomier, and zoomier status wagons. Only these testimonials never found their way into television commercials or onto violently colored posters in trolleys, buses, and subways. Old Fitzgurgle's Bourbon can be made attractive to all sorts of Americans. The concept of "Perspectives Through Literature," evidently, is the wrong kind of corn.

Let me offer one more testimonial, again, as it happens, from a course in the modern novel. This paragraph comes from the final exam of an attractive and perceptive young lady:

One problem which I must confess dismayed me was women's part in society and women's relation to man. Perhaps because I had not had a reading course in college before, I did not realize that this problem existed. I thought that men's views on women's purpose and place in society had changed with the vote for women's suffrage. Obviously after being assailed by the authors on one hand and the masculine members of the class on the other, this is a problem which is not nearly solved. And the trouble is that college educations seem to make matters worse instead of better. In most of the novels the woman's part was dismally servile in comparison to the man. Unless the woman were of the homey, doormat type of Catherine in A *Farewell to Arms* or the pretty but useless decoration of Daisy in *The Great Gatsby*, she ended up the cause of man's troubles, like Marjorie Carling in *Point Counterpoint*, or as ineffectual as Mrs. Dalloway. If this is the period of freedom of the individual advocated by Rupert and Rampion, what happened to the women? The women who were portrayed as wholesome, warm characters were very few. Even Mary Rampion only said the things she had heard Mark express. I don't feel exactly crushed myself, but it certainly makes me feel as though something is wrong when so many conflicts are expressed.

For each of the students I have quoted, literature offers some sort of perspective. Some of the students are so concerned with the pressures of their personal lives that they look to literature for situations comparable to the ones in which they find themselves. Others are able to go to literature for what we like to call "the broader view."

[3] For the entire discussion, see William M. Schutte and Erwin R. Steinberg, "What Good is Literature Anyhow?" *Journal of Higher Education*, June, 1958.

Specifically, then, what sort of perspectives can literature provide for the student of engineering and science or for any student? It can help him to explore important relationships: the relationships between man and his God, between man and his fellow man, and between man and his inner self. Within these broad areas, it can provide subject matter and context for exploring such human problems as:

the relationship of parents and children;
the relationship of men and women, including romantic love;
the relationship of man to the physical world;
the function and nature of religion;
the integrity of the individual;
free will and determinism;
respectability and conventionality;
class distinction;
materialism;
nationalism;
political democracy.

These, of course, are only a few.

I should add here that, although it may sound that way from what I have said, I am not recommending that literature be treated as a social science or be used as a nostrum or patent medicine for what has come to be called bibliotherapy. (Prescription for young man with obvious Oedipus complex: read *The Silver Cord* and take a short course in Philip Wylie. Prescription for illegitimate young lady who does not know who her father is: read *The Scarlet Letter* and *Silas Marner*.) Because I have focused on only one aspect of literature—its value in providing the student with perspective for living—I have stressed what some of you may feel is its utility. I think that we must also help the student to understand the artistic dimension of literature. But I would add quickly that we should approach art through meaning. For if meaning is not literature's only dimension, it is certainly its most important dimension. And through it, we can help the student to understand his fellow man, the world in which he lives, and himself.

SCIENTIST AND HUMANIST: CAN THE MINDS MEET?

I. I. Rabi

1

For more than half a century, from the period of the Darwinian controversy till the end of the 1930s, science remained almost unchallenged as the source of enlightenment, understanding, and hope for a better, healthier, and safer world. The benefits brought by science were and are still visible everywhere one looks. Human ills are being overcome; food supplies are becoming more abundant; travel and communication are quick and easy, and the comforts of life, especially for the common man, are vastly increased. In the person of Albert Einstein science enjoyed a world-wide respect almost akin to reverence and hardly equaled since the time of Isaac Newton.

In the last decade or so we have begun to detect signs of significant change. The knowledge and techniques developed through science for the illumination of the mind and the elevation of the spirit, for the prolongation and the amelioration of life, have been used for the destruction of life and the degradation of the human spirit. Technological warfare, biological warfare, psychological warfare, brainwashing, all make use of science with frightening results.

I do not suggest that warfare and its attendant horror is a result of modern science. Ancient Greece, at the zenith of that remarkable civilization, in a land united by a common culture and a common religion, destroyed itself in a bitter and useless war more thoroughly than Europe has done in the present century even with the aid of electronics, aviation, and high explosives. What I mean is that our epoch in history, which has produced one of the greatest achievements of the human race, may

From *Atlantic Monthly*, CXCVII (1956), 64–67. Reprinted by permission of I. I. Rabi and *Atlantic Monthly*.

be passing into a twilight that does not precede the dawn.

Science, the triumph of the intellect and the rational faculties, has resulted in the hydrogen bomb. The glib conclusion is that science and the intellect are therefore false guides. We must seek elsewhere, some people say, for hope and salvation; but, say the same people, while doing so we must keep ahead of the Russians in technology and in the armaments race. Keep the fearsome fruits but reject the spirit of science. Such is the growing mood of some people at the present time. It is a mood of anti-intellectualism which can only hasten the destruction which these people fear. Anti-intellectualism has always been endemic in every society, perhaps in the heart of every human being. In times of stress this attitude is stimulated and people tend to become impatient and yield to prejudice and emotion just when coolness, subtlety, and reason are most needed.

We are told, and most of us believe, that we are living in a period of crisis unequaled in history. To be cheerful and proud of our accomplishment and optimistic of the future is almost akin to subversion. To be considered objective and realistic, one must view with alarm. Yet we are not living in a period of hard times and unemployment! We have, I cannot say enjoyed but, rather, bemoaned, a period of prosperity and world-wide influence for good unequaled in history. Nevertheless, despite all, we seem to be acquiring a complacency of despair. In this mood, unable to adjust to new values, we hark back to a past which now looks so bright in retrospect, and we raise the banner of "Back to the Humanities."

What is meant by the slogan "Back to the Humanities"? What are people really looking for? What knowledge, what guidance, what hope for salvation, what inspiration, or what relief from anxiety does a practical-minded people like ours expect from a knowledge of the humanities? They do not wish to re-establish the study of the Greek and Roman classics in their original tongues, or to re-create the Greek city-state in Metropolitan Boston.

I venture to suggest that what they mean is something quite different from what is meant by the humanities. The progress of civilization in the modern age, especially in our own century, has brought with it an immense increase of knowledge of every kind, from archaeology to zoology. More is known of the history of antiquity than was known to Herodotus. We have penetrated farther into the heavens and into the innermost secrets of the structure of matter than anyone could have dreamt of in previous generations. We have run through the satisfactions of representational art to the puzzling outlines of abstract art. The increase in physical comfort and in communication has brought with it a whole set of new problems. The great increase in population necessarily means further crowding and additional social and cultural adjustment. Under these circumstances, it is natural for people to look for guidance toward a balanced adjustment.

2

What people are really looking for is wisdom. To our great store of knowledge we need the added quality of wisdom.

Wisdom is inseparable from knowledge; it is knowledge plus a quality which is within the human being. Without it knowledge is dry, almost unfit for human consumption, and dangerous in application. The absence of wisdom is clearly noticeable; the learned fool and the educated bore have been with us since the beginnings of recorded history. Wisdom adds flavor, order, and measure to knowledge. Wisdom makes itself most manifest in the application of knowledge to human needs.

Every generation of mankind has to remake its culture, its values, and its goals. Changing circumstances make older habits and customs valueless or obsolete. New knowledge exposes the limitations and the contingent nature of older philosophies and of previously accepted guides to action. Wisdom does not come in formulas, proverbs, or wise saws, but out of the living actuality. The past is important for understanding the present, but it is not the present. It is in a real sense created in the present, and changes from the point of view of every generation.

When change is slow, the new is gradually assimilated, and only after a number of generations is it noticeable that the world is really different. In our century enormous changes in the circumstances of our lives and in our knowledge have occurred rapidly—in every decade. It is therefore not at all surprising that our intellectual, our social, and our political processes have failed to keep abreast of contemporary problems. It is not surprising that we become confused in the choice of our goals and the paths which we must take to reach them.

Clearly a study of the Greek and Roman classics in their original tongues or even in a good translation is a most rewarding venture in itself. This literature has never been surpassed in any age. And in reading this literature one is struck by how applicable the situations are to the present day. The fact that we can still be moved strongly by this literature is an illustration not merely of the constancy of structure of the human nervous system but also of the fact that great art and profound insights have a character which is independent of any age.

The humanities preserve and create values; even more they express the symbolic, poetic, and prophetic qualities of the human spirit. Without the humanities we would not be conscious of our history; we would lose many of our aspirations and the graces of expression that move men's hearts. Withal the humanities discern but a part of the life of man—true, a vital part but only a part.

It has often been claimed that the chief justification for the study of the humanities is that it teaches us values. In fact some people go even further and claim that the humanities, in which literature, parts of philosophy, and the history and appreciation of the fine arts are included, are the *only* sources of values other than the more spiritual values of religion.

This claim cannot pass without challenge. It cannot be said that it is absurd, but rather that it is a symptom of our failure in the present age to achieve a unity and balance of knowledge which is imbued with wisdom. It is a symptom of both ignorance and a certain anti-rational attitude which has been the curse of our century. It betrays a lack of self-confidence and faith in the greatness of the human spirit in contemporary man. It is the expression of a form of self-hatred which is rationally unjustifiable although deeply rooted.

Man is made of dust and to dust returneth; he lives in a universe of which he is also a part. He is free only in a symbolic sense; his nature is conditioned by the dust out of which he is made. To learn to understand himself he must learn to understand the universe in which he lives. There is more than enough in this enterprise to engage the boldest, the most imaginative, and the keenest minds and spirits of every generation. The universe is not given to us in the form of a map or guide. It is made by human minds and imaginations out of slight hints which come from acute observation and from the profound stratagems of experiments.

How can we hope to obtain wisdom, the wisdom which is meaningful in our own time? We certainly cannot attain it as long as the two great branches of human knowledge, the sciences and the humanities, remain separate and even warring disciplines.

Why is science, even more than the humanities, as a living component of our society so misunderstood? A glance at a current dictionary definition may give us a clue.

Science: "A branch of knowledge dealing with facts or truths systematically arranged and showing the operation of general law."

This definition brings to my mind a solitaire player or head bookkeeper for a mail-order concern. It is a partial truth which is also a caricature. It is out of harmony with the picture of Archimedes jumping out of his bath crying Eureka! or Galileo in misery and degradation during his trial and recantation, or Einstein creating the universe out of one or two deductions from observation and a profound aesthetic feeling for symmetry. Nor does this definition account for the violence of the opposition to scientific discovery which still exists in the same quarters in our own age.

It is often argued that physical science is inherently simple, whereas the study of man is inherently complicated. Yet a great deal is known of man's nature. Wise laws for government and personal conduct were known in remotest antiquity. The literature of antiquity shows a profound understanding of human natures and emotions. Not man but the external world was bewildering. The world of nature instead of seeming simple was infinitely complex and possessed of spirits and demons. Nature had to be worshiped and propitiated by offerings, ceremonies, and prayers. Fundamentally nature was unpredictable, antagonistic to human aspiration, full of significance and purpose, and generally evil. Knowledge of nature was suspect because of the power which it brought, a power which was somehow allied with evil. There were of course always men who had insights far beyond these seemingly naïve notions, but they did not prevail over what seemed to be the evidence of the senses and of practical experience.

It was therefore not until late in the history of mankind, not until a few seconds ago so to speak, that it was recognized that nature is understandable and that a knowledge of nature is good and can be used with benefit; that it does not involve witchcraft or a compact with the devil. What is more, any person of intelligence can understand the ideas involved and with sufficient skill learn the necessary techniques, intellectual and manual.

This idea which is now so commonplace represents an almost complete break with the past. To revere and trust the rational faculty of the mind—to allow no taboo to interfere in its operation, to have nothing immune from its examination—is a new value which has been introduced into the world. The progress of science has been the chief agent in demonstrating its importance and riveting it into the consciousness of mankind. This value does not yet have universal acceptance in this country or in any other country. But in spite of all obstacles it will become one of the most treasured possessions of all mankind because we can no longer live without it. We have gone too far along the direction which it implies ever to turn back without unimaginable disaster.

The last world war was started in an attempt to turn back to dark reaction against the rational faculty and to introduce a new demonology into the world. It failed as will every other such attempt. Once the mind is free it will be destroyed rather than be put back in chains.

3

To my mind the value content of science or literary scholarship lies not in the subject matter alone; it lies chiefly in the spirit and living tradition in which these disciplines are pursued. The spirit is almost always conditioned by the subject. Science and the humanities are not the same thing; the subject matter is different and the spirit and tradition are different. Our problem in our search for wisdom is to blend these two traditions in the minds of individual men and women.

Many colleges and universities are trying to do just this, but there is one serious defect in the method. We pour a little of this and a little of that into the student's mind in proportions which result from mediation between the departments and from the particular predilections of the deans and the president. We then hope that these ingredients will combine through some mysterious alchemy and the result will be a man educated, well-rounded, and wise. Most often, however, these ingredients remain well separated in the compartmentalized mind, or they may form an indigestible precipitate which is not only useless but positively harmful, until time the healer washes it all away.

Wisdom is by its nature an interdisciplinary quality and not the product of a collection of specialists. Although the colleges do indeed try to mold the student toward a certain ideal of the educated man of the twentieth century, it is too often a broad education administered by specialists. The approximate counterpart to this ideal of the educated man, embodied in a real living person, is a rare being on any college faculty. Indeed, in most colleges and universities the student is the only really active connecting link between the different departments. In a certain paradoxical sense the students are the only broadly educated body in the university community, at least in principle.

The affairs of this country—indeed of almost every country —whether in government, education, industry, or business, are controlled by people of broad experience. However, this broad experience rarely includes the field of science. How can our leaders make wise decisions now in the middle of the twentieth century without a deep understanding of scientific thought and feeling for scientific traditions? The answer is clear in the sad course that events have taken.

This anguished thought has impelled many scientists, often to their own personal peril, to concern themselves with matters which in the past were the exclusive domain of statesmen and military leaders. They have tried to advise, importune, and even cajole our leaders to include the scientific factor in our fateful policy decisions. They have been successful, but only in special instances.

I am not making a plea for the scientist statesman comparable to the philosopher king. The scientist rarely has this kind of ambition. The study of nature in its profundity, beauty, and subtlety is too attractive for him to wish to forsake his own creative and rewarding activity. The scientist away from his science is like an exile who longs for the sights and sounds of his native land. What the scientist really desires is for his science to be understood, to become an integral part of our general culture, to be given proper weight in the cultural and practical affairs of the world.

The greatest difficulty which stands in the way of a meeting of the minds of the scientist and the non-scientist is the difficulty of communication, a difficulty which stems from some of the defects of education to which I have alluded. The mature scientist, if he has any taste in these directions, can listen with pleasure to the philosopher, the historian, the literary man, or even to the art critic. There is little difficulty from that side because the scientist has been educated in our general culture and lives in it on a day-to-day basis. He reads newspapers, magazines, books, listens to music, debates politics, and participates in the general activities of an educated citizen.

Unfortunately this channel of communication is often a one-way street. The non-scientist cannot listen to the scientist with pleasure and understanding. Despite its universal outlook and its unifying principle, its splendid tradition, science seems to be no longer communicable to the great majority of educated laymen. They simply do not possess the background of the science of today and the intellectual tool necessary for them to understand what effects science will have on them and on the world. Instead of understanding, they have only a naïve awe mixed with fear and scorn. To his colleagues in the university the scientist tends to seem more and more like a man from another planet, a creature scattering antibiotics with one hand and atomic bombs with the other.

The problems to which I have addressed myself are not particularly American. The same condition exists in England, France, and indeed in all other countries. From my observation we are perhaps better off than most. Our American colleges and universities, since they are fairly recent and are rapidly expanding, have not settled into complacency. They are quite

ready to experiment to achieve desired ends. Our experimental
methods have taught us how to impart the most diverse forms
of knowledge. Although wisdom is more elusive, once the objective is clear that the ultimate end of education is knowledge
imbedded in wisdom we shall find ways to move toward that
ideal. The ideal of the well-rounded man is a meaningless ideal
unless this sphericity means a fusion of knowledge to achieve
balanced judgment and understanding, which are qualities of
wisdom.

The problems are, of course, depressingly difficult. In the
secondary schools—with their overcrowding, their teachers over-
worked and inadequately trained, the school boards, and, not
least, the powerful clique of professional educators who form a
society within our society—all that is unique and characteristic
of science and mathematics is being crowded out of the curriculum and replaced by a fairy tale known as general science. The
colleges and universities are in much better shape, although the
great population increase is about to hit them with masses of
inadequately prepared students. Most people would be quite
content with a holding operation in which we could maintain
the quality that is already possessed.

However, it seems to me that something could be done even
now with the faculty members of the colleges and the universities. Wisdom can achieve a hybrid vigor by crossing the scientist
and the humanist through a more extensive and intensive inter-
action within the faculty. Why should not the professor of
physics be expected to refresh himself periodically by taking a
course in aesthetics or comparative literature or in the Greek
drama? Why shouldn't the professor of medieval philosophy or
the professor of ancient history take a course in modern physics
and become acquainted with the profound thoughts underlying
relativity and quantum mechanics? It would let in some fresh
air, or at least different air, to blow away some of the cobwebs
which grow in the unventilated ivory towers.

Somewhere a beginning has to be made to achieve a more
architectural quality in our culture, a quality of proportion and
of organic unity, and it is reasonable to start with the members
of the faculties of our institutions of higher learning. Here are
all the strands of the tapestry which is to represent our culture,

living in close proximity but separate, adding up to nothing more than the sum of the parts. The scientists must learn to teach science in the spirit of wisdom and in the light of the history of human thought and human effort, rather than as the geography of a universe uninhabited by mankind. Our colleagues in the non-scientific faculties must understand that if their teachings ignore the great scientific tradition and its accomplishments, their words, however eloquent and elegant, will lose meaning for this generation and be barren of fruit.

Only with a united effort of science and the humanities can we hope to succeed in discovering a community of thought which can lead us out of the darkness and the confusion which oppress all mankind.

THE TREE OF KNOWLEDGE

Robert Oppenheimer

[In April Dr. Oppenheimer spoke to a group of editors and journalists from all over the world who had gathered in Washington for a meeting of the International Press Institute. He spoke without a prepared text, using only notes; the article which follows is published substantially as it was recorded during the lecture.]

When I speak to the press I am aware that I am talking to a group of men who have a singularly critical destiny in these rather peculiar times. Those of us whose work it is to preserve old learning, and to find new, look to the press to keep the channels of truth and communication open and to keep men in some sense united in common knowledge and common humanity.

I want to talk about the nature and structure of our knowledge today and how it has altered and complicated the problems of the press. There are enormous differences between our world of learning today—our Tree of Knowledge—and those of

From *Harper's* (October, 1958), 55–60. Reprinted by permission of Robert Oppenheimer and *Harper's*.

Athens, or the Enlightenment, or the dawn of science in fif-
teenth- and sixteenth-century Europe. You can get some suggestion of how shattering these changes have been if you remember that Plato, when he tried to think about human salvation
and government, recommended mathematics as one of the ways
to learn to know the truth, to discriminate good from evil and
the wise from the foolish. Plato was not a creative mathematician, but students confirm that he knew the mathematics of
his day, and understood it, and derived much from it.

Today, it is not only that our kings do not know mathematics,
but our philosophers do not know mathematics and—to go a
step further—our mathematicians do not know mathematics.
Each of them knows a branch of the subject and they listen to
each other with a fraternal and honest respect; and here and
there you find a knitting together of the different fields of mathematical specialization. In fact, a great deal of progress in mathematics is a kind of over-arching generalization which brings
things that had been separate into some kind of relation. Nevertheless, it is not likely today that our most learned advisers—the
men who write in the press and tell us what we may think—
would suggest that the next President of the United States be
able to understand the mathematics of the day.

YIELDING BOUNDARIES

The first characteristic of scientific knowledge today—a trivial
and pedestrian characteristic—is that its growth can be measured. When I talk of "science" here I would like to use the
word in the broadest sense to include all man's knowledge of his
history and behavior, his knowledge, in fact, of anything that
can be talked of in an objective way so that people all over the
world can understand it, know what the scientist has done, re-
produce it, and find out if it is true or not. It is hard to measure
the growth of science defined in these terms in a sensible way
but it can be measured in fairly foolish ways.

One way of measuring science, for example, is to find out how
many people are engaged in it. I know a young historian of science who has amused himself by counting the scientists of the
last two centuries and he has found that their number has, quite
accurately, doubled about every ten years. Professor Purcell of

Harvard put the same conclusion another way the other day when he said, "Ninety per cent of all scientists are alive." This gives some notion of the changes involved.

I must, however, qualify this trend in two ways. First, it cannot continue, because if it went on for another century, then everyone would be a scientist—there would be nobody else left. So a kind of saturation is setting in and the rate of science's growth is slowing down. The second qualification is that what might be called the "stature" of science is not proportional to its volume; it may be proportional to the cube root of its volume or something like that. In short, every scientist is not a Newton and the proportion of Newtons among all scientists tends to decline as the number of people involved gets bigger.

Despite all qualification, though, the fact remains that the growth in the number of people in science and the growth in firm knowledge—important, non-trivial knowledge of the kind that appears in learned journals and books—have been more or less parallel; and this growth will continue, although the increase in it is bound to taper off. The result is that nearly everything that is now known was not in any book when most of us went to school; we cannot know it unless we have picked it up since. This in itself presents a problem of communication that is nightmarishly formidable.

On the other hand, there is a more encouraging aspect of this scientific knowledge. As it grows, things, in some ways, get much simpler. They do not get simpler because one discovers a few fundamental principles which the man in the street can understand and from which he can derive everything else. But we do find an enormous amount of order. The world is not random and whatever order it has seems in large part "fit," as Thomas Jefferson said, for the human intelligence. The enormous variety of facts yields to some kind of arrangement, simplicity, generalization.

One great change in this direction—and it has not yet, I think, fully come to public understanding—is that we are beginning to see that the hard boundaries which once seemed to separate the parts of the natural world from each other are now yielding to some kind of inquiry. We are beginning to see ways across the gaps between the living and the dead, the physical and the mental.

Let me give just a few illustrations:

It is probably not an accident, although it is not really understood, that the age of the earth—some six or seven billion years according to calculation by radioactive techniques—is very close to the period required for the most distant nebulae to recede into the furthest reaches of space. We can picturesquely define that time by saying that during it things were a lot closer together than they are now and the state of the material universe was very different. Some years ago the brilliant Russian biochemist Oparin suggested that when the atmosphere had no oxygen in it, certain conditions could have prevailed on earth under which life could have originated from inorganic matter. There has since been confirmation in Urey's laboratory and this hypothesis turns out to be true. Although mermaids and heroes do not walk out of the test tube, we do see that quite reasonable accounts of the origin of life are not too far from our grasp.

The recent research on how the genetic mechanisms of all living material operate shows how certain proteins have special information-bearing properties—how they can store information and transmit it from one generation to another.[1]

The study of how the nerve impulses from our sense organs to the brain can be modulated and altered by the perceptive apparatus of the animal—often it is an animal rather than a man—give us some notion both of the unreliability of our sense impressions and of the subtlety of the relations between thought and the object of thought.

All these problems, which even in the nineteenth century seemed to obstruct the possibility of a unified view of the great arch of nature, are yielding to discovery; and in all science there is a pervasive, haunting sense that no part of nature is really irrelevant to any other.

GAY AND WONDERFUL MYSTERY

But the model of science which results from all this investigation is entirely different from a model which would have seemed natural and understandable to the Greeks or the Newtonians. Although we do start from common human experience, as they did, we so refine what we think, we so change the meaning of words, we build up so distinctive a tradition, that scien-

---

[1] An account of this development, by F.H.C. Crick, appeared in *Scientific American*, September 1957.

tific knowledge today is not an enrichment of the general culture. It is, on the contrary, the possession of countless, highly specialized communities who love it, would like to share it, would very much like to explain it, and who make some efforts to communicate it; but it is not part of the common human understanding. This is the very strange predicament to which the press addresses itself today and to which it can give, I believe, only a partial solution.

It would of course be splendid—and one often hears this—if we could say that while we cannot know the little details about the workings of atoms and proteins and the human psyche, we *can* know the fundamental principles of science. But I am afraid that this is only marginally true. The fundamentals of physics are defined in terms of words that refer to an experience that lay people have not had and that very few people have run across in their education.

For example, in my opinion, it is almost impossible to explain what the fundamental principle of relativity is about, and this is even more true of the quantum theory. It is only possible to use analogies, to evoke some sense of understanding. And as for the recent discovery—the very gay and wonderful discovery for which Dr. Yang and Dr. Lee were awarded the Nobel Prize— that nature has a preference for right-handed or left-handed screws in certain situations and is not indifferent to the handedness of the screw—to explain this is, I believe, quite beyond my capacity. And I have never heard anyone do it in a way that could be called an enrichment of culture.

To sum up the characteristics of scientific knowledge today, then, I would say that it is mostly new; it has not been digested; it is not part of man's common knowledge; it has become the property of specialized communities who may on occasion help one another but who, by and large, pursue their own way with growing intensity further and further from their roots in ordinary life.

We must always remember that, like most human accomplishments, the sciences have grown out of a long, accumulating experience of error, astonishment, invention, and understanding. Taken as a whole, they constitute a series of traditions; and these traditions—once largely common, now largely separate—

are as essential to understanding a part of biology or astronomy or physics as the general human tradition is to the existence of civilized life. I know that a complete immersion in these many different, related, yet specific traditions is beyond the reach of any one person—that as things stand today, most of us are without any experience, really, in any. We have much in common from the simple ways in which we have learned to live and talk and work together. Out of this have grown the specialized disciplines like the fingers of the hand, united in origin but no longer in contact.

PRACTICAL BOOBY TRAPS

Now I am going to make a distinction which may seem arbitrarily sharp but which is I think important both to the learned community and the press. I have been talking until now about science as the things we have discovered about nature—incredible things and beautiful and astonishing, but defined, usually, not by any use to which they are put, but simply in terms of the ways in which they were found out. Pure science is thus inherently circumscribed but immensely revealing, showing as it does that left to itself, man's imagination was not a patch on reality.

Seeking out this knowledge is one problem and I am not through with it. But the other problem is that, of course, this knowledge has practical consequences. On it is built the world we live in and the face of that world has been changed, probably more than in any other period of history, by the scientific revolution. Now these practical consequences, because they are intended in some way to be responsive to man's needs, can be talked about in an intelligible way. It is not necessary to know how a nucleus is put together, or what are the laws which determine its behavior, in order to explain what nuclear energy is all about. It may be very hard to explain it well because it involves human choices, options, decisions, prejudices. But I believe that it is no more difficult to write about nuclear energy than about where people go for a holiday. It is not much harder to write about nuclear weapons, except that, to the problems of human variety, there is added the problem of a very great deal of secrecy.

To take another example, it has not been hard to write about the use of vaccines in the prevention of disease and these can be described without elaborate theory. As a matter of fact the vaccines were discovered without much theoretical background and the atomic bomb was made before we had much idea what held nuclei together; we do not have very much idea today.

The press has done an admirable job in explaining these and other practical applications of science—I think it is aware that it has to do a much, much greater one. But there are, I think, some booby traps which stand in its way. I would like to list three of them.

One of the simplest traps is that when technical people talk they always emphasize the fact that they are not sure. Sometimes, as in the case of knowing all the effects of radiation on life, we are not, in fact, sure, because experience takes so long to acquire. But usually the statement that we are not sure is more like the polite comment, "I don't want to bore you but . . ." Statements about scientific matters are not entirely sure—nothing is—but compared to politics they are so extremely sure as to be of a different order of certainty. If a scientist says he is not sure, pay attention to the limits within which he says this—the margin for error he insists on allowing. This margin will not be so wide. Within what limits we are uncertain about the genetic damages of radiation, for example, is not something to worry or wonder about. We know something of the effects on the genes. The differences of opinion over this question lie in quite a different field. They lie in conflicting assessments of the relative gravity of these damages and of other vaster dangers of total nuclear war.

A second trap to beware of is the strange fact that the words scientists use have taken on special meaning so that there is a confusing quality of punning when they discuss technical things and describe their aims. "Relativity" sounds like something that occurs in daily life; it is not. Scientists talk about the "adventure" of science and they are right; but of course in the public mind this is very likely to be identified with looking to see if the other side of the moon is really there. Here the public is wrong. The adventures of science are intellectual adventures, involving discoveries of the inadequacy of our means of describing nature, because it is so unfamiliar and strange. Space travel has, no doubt, its value and virtue, but it is in no way related to the great adventures of science. It would be, of course, if we could go out two or three billion light-years and see what is going on there, because it is hard to see that far with telescopes. But this is not the same thing as the progress of human learning and understanding.

A third trap and a serious one—it has infested the discussion of radioactive fallout—is that in most technical explanations, very large numbers occur, and it is often hard to convey their implications sensitively. It may be equally true to say, for instance, that something will cause 10,000 casualties and that these casualties will affect a hundred-thousandth of the population of the world; but one statement can make the effect seem rather small and the other can make it very big. We cannot get over the habit of talking in numbers but it takes some exposition if we are to avoid creating the wrong impression.

I have one example of this. It has to do with radioactive fallout. I know nothing about the main efforts being made to eliminate fallout at present but it is obvious that they have to do with the elimination of fissionable material from bombs. The first step is to take the casing away from big bombs and the next step, presumably, is to take away much—or even all—of the rest.

I have some understanding of this as a technical problem and some idea of the benefits which will accrue from it. But in an old day, when we had the first primitive, tiny, atomic weapons, there was also a contrast. The story is in the public domain and I am surprised that no reporter has dug it out. We were thinking then in terms of casualties of hundreds of thousands and not hundreds of millions. It was a much more innocent age but it was warfare and in that sense it was not innocent. All the bombs then had fissionable material and the first one we set off at Trinity near Los Alamos was dirty. It was set off practically at ground level, the fireball touched the ground and in fact a great deal of radioactive contamination was spread, by the standard of those days. The government had a lot of trouble with a herd of cattle whose hair turned white as a result. It was a very dirty bomb.

The bombs at Hiroshima and Nagasaki on the other hand were clean. They were exploded high in the air and few if any casualties were produced by fallout. Possibly there were a handful on a global scale, but practically all the hundreds of thousands who died, and the others who were maimed from radiation and blast, did not have the benefit of fallout. Nevertheless, I vastly prefer our first dirty bomb to those two clean ones.

When all is said and done about these problems—essentially soluble problems—of describing the practical consequences of scientific progress, there remains the central, perplexing question, to which I keep returning, of bringing an appreciation of the new scientific knowledge to the world. It is a question of high importance; it deserves study.

I do not see, for example, how the scientist can evoke the same understanding and grateful warmth from his fellows as the actor who gives them pleasure and insight, and reveals their own predicament to them, or the musician or dancer or writer or athlete, in whom they see their talents in greater perfection, and often their own limitations and error in larger perspective. The power of the new knowledge itself to excite the intelligent public's mind is very different from the days of Newton when the problems under discussion—the course of the heavenly bodies, the laws of dynamics—were not far from ordinary human experience. People could go to demonstrations to see the new principles in action; they could discuss them in salons and cafés. The ideas were revolutionary but not very hard to understand. It is no wonder that the excitement and change and enrichment of culture in Europe that came about as a result of these discoveries were without parallel.

Today there are sciences like that, which are just starting. During the nineteenth century the theory of evolution certainly played this role. And today, in the psychological sciences there are many fundamental points that anyone can understand if he is willing to take the trouble—science here is just beginning to leave the common experience, and the accumulated tradition has not yet grown very far.

Yet as a whole, the problem is formidable. It is not hopeless —much can and should be done. But I do not believe it can be done by the press alone. Part of the solution lies in education, and, I think, part of it lies with just learning to live with it. Our tradition and culture and community of learning have become reticulated, complicated, and non-hierarchal. They have their own nobility if one brings to them the right attitudes of affection, interest, and indefatigability. The new knowledge is not the kind of thing one can ever finally master; there is no place a man can go to get it all straight. But it has its beauty if one knows how to live with it. And the main thing is to recognize this and not to talk in terms of cultures which are unattainable for us, but to welcome those that are at hand.

Because beyond the need for explanation of the practical, beyond the need for information, there will always be the need for a community of meaning and understanding. To my mind this is a basic and central need. It is a very grave circumstance of our time that the overwhelming part of new knowledge is available only to a few people and does not enrich common understanding. I think, nevertheless, that learned folk do have some sense of this community; and I think this furnishes a clue for others, because it comes in part from the similarities of experience in our professional lives—from recognizing points in common and differences in our separate traditions. We have lived in parallel ways through experience and wonder and have some glimmering of a kind of new-found harmony.

This suggests to me that all of us in our years of learning, and many if not most of us throughout our lives, need some true apprenticeship, some hard and concentrated work, in the specialized traditions. This will make us better able to understand one another but, most important of all, it will clarify for us the extent to which we do not understand one another. It will not be easy. It means a major change in the way we look at the world and in our educational practices. It means that an understanding of the scope, depth, and nature of our ignorance should be among the primary purposes of education. But to me, it seems necessary for the coherence of our culture, and for the very future of any free civilization. A faithful image of this in the public press could do a great deal to help us all get on with it.

THE HUMANITIES AND THE COMMON READER

Howard Mumford Jones

The humanities, whatever is meant by that baffling term, seem to the musing observer to offer a succession of paradoxes. The word itself is a modern invention, coming to us from the nineteenth century. One might reasonably infer that, given so recent a coinage, we must know what we mean by it. In fact, however, we do not quite know what we mean by it, and this is the first paradox. We believe in something we cannot delimit. Probably the only safe working definition of the humanities is this: "You know horses—cows are different." You know the sciences, the humanities are different. They are what you have left in the college curriculum when you extract the sciences— natural, physical, and social.

Or are they? Huxley was neither the first nor the last great man to claim that science, nobly pursued, offers a humane mode of education, and I, for one, am quite ready to admit his claim. As for the social sciences, if the object of humane·learning is man; and if man is, as he seemed to Aristotle to be, a political animal; and if the social sciences have anything wise to say about him as a political animal, and I think they do, I find it difficult to keep up the proper humanistic irreverence for the social sciences. For example, I am not convinced that sociology is any more plagued by jargon than is philological lore, literary criticism, or contemporary aesthetics. Novelists and poets there have been who were also wise men, but novelists and poets are not always wise, and I am unable to grasp the logic which argues that because Plato and Shakespeare are wise men, therefore contemporary social psychologists must be shal-

From Julian Harris, ed., *The Humanities.* Copyright 1950 by the Regents of the University of Wisconsin. Reprinted by permission of the Regents of the University of Wisconsin.

low and wrong. This is too much like scorning the typewriter because it was not used by Homer.

Is history one of the humanities, or is it one of the social sciences? Is the theory of the state in Dante to be considered forever valuable because it is in literary form, whereas cultural anthropology is to remain only a passing fashionable craze? Sometimes humanistic scholars argue as if they thought so. May I remind you of a scholar named Francis Bacon who, seeing great hopes for man kind in empirical science, also said that undue reverence for "authority" is one of the peccant humors of learning?

We do not, then, really know what we mean by the humanities, and this very uncertainty perhaps leads us to be a little bit arrogant about our claims for our own priority in wisdom. We do not, in fact, really know whether we can distinguish a peculiar body of lore or wisdom or organized knowledge as something uniquely ours. Of course the professional humanist will seldom admit that this is so, but in fact I think it *is* so, and I am inclined to believe that a little more intellectual humility among scholars in discussing each other's specialties would be a valuable practical example of the ripe fruits of humane discipline.

But let me pass to a second paradox. If it is hard to separate humane learning from all other sorts of learning, another contradiction puzzles me. The humanities, whatever else they are, are highly educational, so much so that they have their principal, and perhaps their only, home in educational institutions, whereas the sciences spill over into industry and government, and the social sciences spill over into business, government, and social welfare. If the colleges and universities were to shut down tomorrow, I think the sciences and the social sciences, though they would be injured, could get along, but in that event I am not clear that the humanities could get along, unless they took refuge in public libraries. They are, it would seem, quintessentially bookish and also quintessentially part of the educational process. The great humanists, the great humanist documents prove ever and again to be consciously educational.

This being so, a man from Mars might reasonably infer that education, particularly education in the democratic state, a state wherein the responsibilities for decision rest, even if they rest indirectly, upon every citizen, would be a matter of primary concern to humanists. He would infer, for example, that if there is a subject called education, if the training of teachers seems essential to the health of the commonwealth, education must be one of the humanities, and the enlisting, training, and honoring of teachers, particularly public school teachers, would be of immediate concern to humanists. I need not remind you, however, that the man from Mars is in for a terrible shock. He will discover that professional educational training is carried forward in special schools for which all good humanists express unmitigated contempt, that when school teachers come into humanistic courses for training, as they do in our summer sessions, it is fashionable to treat them with a sort of good-humored tolerance, and that you do not awaken any genuine pedagogical enthusiasm in the humanist unless you propose that he train young persons to be scholars like himself. Then, indeed, his zeal awakes, then he really dedicates himself to an educational cause, the cause of the graduate school. Yet so remote in fact is the responsibility, even then, for any direct educational training among humanistic research workers that the graduate schools of the country have, until very recently, refused to recognize that young doctors of philosophy in the humanities are not going directly into research libraries, but into classrooms where their first job is to teach high school graduates, the majority of whom are not going to be humanistic specialists.

The scholar, of course, has his defense. The defense is that those pernicious and windy fellows, the professors of education, do not understand subject matter, but only formulae. They teach teachers to teach. This the humanist will not do. For him, teaching is a by-product. Teaching is something you learn to do indirectly, through some professional trade secret not revealed to any but the catechumens. And with this excoriation of schools of education and of the badness of our civil pedagogy, the humanist rests his case.

I venture to suggest that the greatest teachers of mankind—Buddha, Socrates, Jesus, Epictetus, Tolstoy, Emerson, whom you will—got along rather well without a Ph.D. They had no printed bibliographies, they demanded no term papers, and they were not, like Charles Eliot Norton, overwhelmed by melancholy because there were no gentlemen in the class. They seem to have concerned themselves, so far as I can make out, rather directly with the education of what we quaintly call the common man and with the training of teachers to teach him. They commanded their followers to become fishers of men rather than fishers of symbolic logic, or aesthetics, or philology, or the *Cambridge Bibliography of English Literature*. And if I am shamelessly, in this question-begging manner, taking advantage of your good nature by a preposterous collocation of unlike things, it is not because I do not respect the *Cambridge Bibliography of English Literature*, philological learning, greatness in art, and the ontological argument for God. Rather, what I am trying to do is to shock you into a sense of how the aristocratic spirit which lurks in scholarship, the samurai spirit of specialism, has carried us away from the rather central problem of the education of the human race.

And this skillfully brings me to my third paradox. To make it clear, I am going to talk for a time as if literary studies and the humanities were interchangeable terms, which they are not, and I am going to seem to find fault with a book which, in fact, I admire. This book is *Theory of Literature* by Messrs. Wellek and Warren, published last winter, a clear, careful, compact, perspicuous cyclopaedia from which you can learn where we stand today in the theory and practice of the higher study of one of the arts. The authors seem to have read and digested everything. There is, for instance, a chapter on the study of euphony, rhythm, and meter, and it is a good chapter. There is one on style and stylistics—I had to find out that this last term is a technical word for investigations into "all devices which aim at some specific expressive end and thus [it] embraces far more than literature or even rhetoric." In this chapter you will find succinct accounts of where we stand today in our knowledge of matters like "expressive value," "sentence pattern," the analysis of linguistic systems, sound schemes, periphrastic vocabularies, and like technical problems. In a world which includes, as Robinson says, both bugs and emperors, there is room for this sort of study, and I am glad it is intelligently pursued.

What *is* literature as a living institution? Or, to bring the matter home, what *is* literature as a living institution in the United States?

Perhaps the book will tell us. I open it at the chapter entitled "Image, Metaphor, Symbol, Myth" and read at random this passage:

> Rhetoricians like Quintilian already make much of the distinction between the metaphor which animates the inanimate, and that which inanimates the animate; but they present the distinction as one between rhetorical devices. With [Dr. Hermann] Pongs . . . it becomes a grandiose contrast between polar attitudes—that of the mythic imagination, which projects personality upon the outer world of things, which animizes and animates nature, and the contrary type of imagination, which feels its way into the alien, which de-animizes or unsubjectivizes itself. All the possibilities of figurative expression are exhausted by these two, the subjective and objective poles.

A footnote tells us that Dr. Pongs "calls the first of his types the *Beseeltypus* and the second the *Erfühltypus*. The first animizes or anthropomorphizes; the second emphasizes."

Is this literature, is this literary study as a living institution in the United States? The answer is not easy, but it is not necessarily "no," nor am I trying to ridicule Dr. Pongs, or Quintilian, or Messrs. Wellek and Warren. Within its own universe of discourse, this somewhat complex prose makes perfectly good sense; and as there should somewhere be a group of persons, however small, passionately devoted to metaphor and style, I should, for one, vigorously defend Dr. Pongs's right to a theory, just as I should vigorously defend Messrs. Wellek and Warren for presenting this theory in clear and admirable English. But if it be true that to a tiny fraction of our population the problem of whether metaphor animizes or de-animizes discourse is a matter of absorbing interest, it is also patent that to the vaster proportion of our population, this problem is of no interest whatsoever. And this vast majority, though it includes the ignorant and the illiterate and the barbarian, includes also the majority of educated men and women, to whom books and the pleasure of reading are part of an intelligent and cultivated life. The patrons of our bookstores, the

readers of our weekly book reviews, the members of the various
book-of-the-month clubs, the subscribers to rental libraries, and,
in sum, the whole body of our reading public, without whose
sanction there can be no literature at all, have, with obvious but
rare exceptions, no interest in this talk about polar attitudes,
mythic imagination, and unsubjectivizing metaphors. They are
willing to have this sort of thing in the schools out of a blind
and flattering belief that scholarship is beyond them anyway
and that this bookish theoric is all well enough for the university classroom and for something mysterious called "learning."

Well, that there should be something mysterious called
learning is something no wise man will dispute. But learning
for what? Learning for whom? Learning to what relevant end?
The vocabulary of Messrs. Wellek and Warren is admirable
for purposes of learning, in the sense that it is intelligible to
learned men. But it is also a technological vocabulary, the
product of some decades of scholarly research, which is in its
way as incomprehensible to the cultivated reader as is the
vocabulary of nuclear physics. In fact, we have as scholars been
carrying on a series of technical operations in language and
literature so delicate and complex that it takes the neophyte
a long time merely to master the significance of the words we
use. And latterly, especially in the twentieth century, we have
carried our technical operations out of what we vaguely call
scholarship into what we vaguely call criticism. Thus, from a
recent anthology of criticism I cull such phrases as these: "the
sporadic intuition of artists," "controlling feeling through
metaphor," "the ideal spectator," "details that are lyrically im-
pure," "pseudo-reference," "the poem is oblique," "a certain
degree of contradiction between tenor and vehicle," "scraps
fuse into integer," "rich and intuitive use of Christian imagery,"
unable "to say what machinery erects a staircase on a contradiction," "ironic tension in poetry," "simultaneity of perception
. . . by breaking up temporal sequence." These are characteristic phrases, picked at random. Of course I do them injustice; of course, by taking them out of context, I have given
them a nudity they do not deserve; of course, if the critic
is to penetrate far into the subtle psychology of the creative
process and the perceptive mind, the old, worn critical phrases

will not do, and he must invent new ones. But it is precisely to the quality of these invented phrases that I call your attention. To the common reader, most of these phrases—excellent no doubt in their places in the essays which contain them, casting for the adept few a real light on literary subtleties—most of these phrases are as opaque as the vocabulary of higher mathematics. And he concludes that if the literary experts are thus unable to make things clear to him, why should he bother with them? However intense and serious to the academician the theory of criticism may seem to be, to the many, books are still a recreation, are for one's idle times, are, indeed, a luxury. What they want out of books is delight and guidance, not conundrums.

I am far from saying that the common reader is necessarily right. If anybody wants to murmur that there is no royal road to humanistic learning, I shall not object. Nevertheless, literary scholarship and literary criticism have grown into curiously technological affairs; and from what little I know about aesthetic theory now governing painting and music, this is also becoming technological, at least from the point of view of the common listener, the common beholder. And, as I once occupied a penthouse owned by an expert in symbolic logic, I can testify, from having tried to read in his library, that large areas of modern metaphysical speculation seem to be more technological still. The one branch of the humanities which has not developed this technological density seems to be history. I find it possible to read history, just as the common reader reads it, with my expectation of plain communication between writer and reader amply fulfilled.

Confronting this implied reproach, the humanist may retort that he has no monopoly on technological talk. If this be an offense, he may say, scientists offend more deeply. But here, I think, we must distinguish. The technological talk of the scientists is aimed at other scientists; it does not pretend, like literary criticism or books on ethics or treatises on art, to be aimed also at the general reader. The universe of discourse of the natural and physical sciences grows daily more complex and requires a complex vocabulary in which to communicate its ideas, whereas there is no special reason to suppose that

the psychology of artistic creation has changed a very great
deal since the time of the Greeks or to believe that the general
principles of morality and metaphysics have in a thousand
years undergone very much of a revolution. Men are still
nominalists or realists, monists or dualists, believers in em-
piricism or trusters in the absolute, theists, atheists, materialists,
skeptics, or agnostics as they were in Athens or Alexandria. For
if the thoughts of the mighty dead are, indeed, obsolete, we
have been wasting a great many valuable man-hours in the
classroom pretending that antiquarianism was life itself. The
humanist cannot have it both ways. He cannot insist that the
works of the past are still virtually as valuable as ever they
were and simultaneously declare that these works have never
been understood until, equipped with modern criticism, modern philology, modern scholarship, truth dawns on us here in
the United States in the year nineteen hundred and what you
please. I do not deny that some among us know a great deal
more about the middle ages than did the eighteenth century
dilettanti or that our views of the classical past are in all
probability juster than those which prevailed at the court of
Charles the Great. But are the insights, the values, the canons
of the common reader any juster? This, from the point of view
of the health of a liberal society, is truly the question to put
to the humanists. And if the scholar says that what he does
at the top of the intellectual pyramid will, he hopes, trickle
down to the masses at the bottom, the common reader cannot
but think that trickling down is a rather amateurish, not to say
uncertain, mode of distributing the treasures the humanists
claim to have stored up for him.

The common reader has, indeed, been standing patiently
by while I have gone off on this long excursion suggested by
the admirable volume of Messrs. Wellek and Warren. Who is
the common reader? He (or she) is the common voter, the high
school graduate, the college alumnus, the sober citizen who
gives what he can to the Community Fund, tries to weigh the
claims of contending parties for his vote, participates in meetings of the Parent-Teachers' Association, supports the colleges
(and incidentally the humanists) through his gifts and taxes,
and tries, by subscribing to magazines and reading books, to

inform himself about men, manners, and opinions. For him, incorrigibly if you like, a novel is supposed to tell a story. For him, regrettably perhaps, poetry is expected to support or to console; and if he can make nothing out of sprung rhythm or Mr. Eliot's "Four Quartets," he has read, let us say, *A Shropshire Lad* and he likes—as who does not?—Benét's fine narrative poem, *John Brown's Body*. As for philosophy, I am afraid he is, or at any rate his wife is, a reader of Rabbi Liebman's *Peace of Mind*, which he has bought in great quantities, just as he has bought Mr. Churchill's memoirs and Mr. Sherwood's book on Harry Hopkins. If a Shakespeare play comes along, let us say Olivier's film of *Hamlet*, he is likely to go to it with his wife and to have some rather fresh views on the production; and I have even seen him in the gallery of a modern art show and sat next to him at a symphony concert. By and large, in the long run, directly or indirectly, he is, is he not, the man whom, in the liberal state, our humanistic studies are primarily designed to influence. We can of course pretend that humanistic scholarship is supported now as it has been supported in the past by wealthy aristocrats, but by and large this is no longer true, and the support of patrons as questionable as Catherine the Great, Pope Alexander VI, or Alcibiades, to stick to the safely dead, is, I have always thought, a rather awkward argument for humanism. No, our present wealth is the wealth of foundations giving out money for social ends, our institutions are tax-supported or kept alive by social campaigns among the alumni, and we are, in sum, committed for our lives and fortunes to the belief of the common reader that we somehow do him good.

I agree that we do him good. We keep alive something called a tradition. We have a great amount of "knowledge about," which is sometimes almost a substitute for knowledge. We help to civilize his offspring, and we persuade a tiny fraction of them to become scholars like ourselves. Without us, the common reader's knowledge of the past would be nebulous indeed. But I am not persuaded, and I think the common reader is not persuaded, that we have richly fulfilled the duties tradition lays upon us.

I do not quite know what is meant by that vague word

"tradition." But I suggest, in the light of the considerations I have urged, that it is not so much the humanist tradition which should concern us as it is the traditional humanist. He has, like the god Janus, a double face. He is simultaneously teacher and scholar. Each of his functions is necessary, the one having its obligation primarily to the learning without which modern society cannot exist, the other having its obligation primarily to society, without which learning cannot exist. But I suggest that the development of our expertized culture has developed the first of these functions out of all proportion to our needs and that we need now to return upon the other function and see what we can do to enrich it for ordinary people—for, to continue my metaphor, the common reader.

The paradox of learning, or rather of the learned man, is patently that in proportion as his expert knowledge increases, his general range diminishes, or is likely to diminish unless he is a very great man indeed. So-and-so has his specialty—American literature, baroque art, literary criticism, Hegelian metaphysics, Alexandrian inscriptions from India—and he naturally desires to enrich his knowledge and to convey his enthusiasm to others. Hence the extraodinary rise of specialisms in American universities, which, if they have increased "knowledge about," have not necessarily increased knowledge, because too often they diminish judgment. They diminish judgment by virtue of the fact that book, document, or object is perpetually interposed as a screen between judgment and direct experience of life. In truth, to change the figure, as our lore grows in quantity, we resemble an army with a baggage train constantly increasing, so that we drag at each remove a lengthening chain.

Efforts to correct this evil—and evil it is—efforts to plunge the masterpiece once more into the living stream of experience from whence it once took form, are constant and commendable. They appear as heroic simplifications—great books, general education, "criticism," the history of culture, the tutorial system, an honors seminar—and it would be idle to deny that these changes have accomplishment to their credit. But they are nevertheless alterations in pattern and machinery; they do not drive directly enough at men. They do not, in sum, guarantee us the kind of teacher we need.

The teacher: whence comes he? How find him? How train him? How persuade him steadfastly to believe that the living personality has an enchantment the library, with all its magic, can never own? Dr. Johnson reminded his readers that if Shakespeare's practice was contrary to the rules of criticism, there was always an appeal open from criticism to nature; and it is in the inability to make the appeal from theory to nature that humanistic teaching is principally at fault. We are bound up with our own books. We do not sufficiently inquire whether the poem, the string quartet, the sculpture, the canvas is likely to please many and please long by its just representation of general nature in terms which the intelligent, but not expert, beholder can be pleased with; we are so deeply absorbed by category and technique, form and pattern that we cannot put down the book except to run to another book in order to bulwark our judgment. Our weakness is to mistake debate among scholars for that appeal to general nature which Johnson made the test of Shakespeare's greatness. And note that Johnson tested the quality of greatness by general nature and not, as too many specialists do, general nature by the quality of bookish greatness.

All parts of the university feel the want of teachers, but this defect is most signal among the humanities. To discuss whether present patterns in education among our graduate schools are likely to produce teachers and to revivify the notion of the teacher as a man speaking to man would take us far afield. Not philology, not criticism, not accuracy, not bibliographical range, not casuistry, not expert knowledge of iconography or of musical form, each excellent in itself, offers inherent guarantee that a new and powerful teacher has stepped upon the stage of the world. Nor, at the other extreme, is a sentimental aversion to intellectual thoroughness any better guarantee. The teacher is not book-bound, but a lover of life. He is unmoved by the psychology of terror or dispute. He reads every scripture in the light of the times which brought it forth, but he does not therefore mistake past prejudice and present fashion for eternity. His faith is life, not the shadow of life cast by the arts, glorious though they are in certain moods and hours. He does not dwell on the seacoast of Bohemia. He knows that books are good, that pictures, music, systems, language are good also, but that they are for times and seasons. If the exquisite and the exotic appeal, if intellectual dexterity has its glitter and its charm, he remains unshaken in the observation that the great human issues are common, coarse and solid; as, death, birth, sex, children, food. He breathes not in the thin air of libraries, decanting out-of-print comedy, tragedy, realism, and romance; instead, if he be dark of soul, his pessimism is bracing, and if of another stripe of spirit, he gives out a joyful and enduring sagacity. Gladly he accepts the injunction of Turgenief: "Simplify! simplify!" since, without derogating from the specialists, he is also enough of a child of Lincoln to know that, in one sense at least, it is in the general classroom that we shall greatly win or meanly lose the last best hope of man.

This is, I know, that rhetoric which blurs distinctions; yet if the humanist tradition springs from the spirit of man, how shall we discourse of the great teacher except spiritually? But that you may not dismiss me as a mere poet, I offer two concrete suggestions for the improvement of the tradition of humanistic teaching. The first is that we radically reduce the number of persons to be admitted to our graduate schools for professional humanistic training, and by this reduction achieve, I hope, a competition for place which will gradually weed out those blameless mediocrities now furnishing too large a fraction of our Ph.D.'s. If we really went at the problem of admitting students to graduate training as the Guggenheim Foundation goes at the problem of ascertaining what ten among a hundred applicants are worth the human energy about to be expended on them; if by interview and test, evidence of others, and performance by the candidate we undertook to screen our catechumens with half the intelligence that publishers use to award prizes or that juries employ in awarding certain famous fellowships, we should not wonder long that humanistic teaching is flaccid and jejune. Our mistaken kindness is twofold: the fact that anybody wants to study under us is flattering; the moral excellence of the applicant (usually conceived of negatively), is wrongly regarded as a surrogate for moral vigor, intellectual achievement, and emotional stability.

My second practical suggestion is equally simple, equally revolutionary, and equally logical. If humanistic studies deal with the whole man, let us ascertain that we have the whole man before us to educate. The soundest part of the theory of Cecil Rhodes, whatever its deficiencies in administration, was that which insisted on the wholeness of personality among the applicants. The test in that case was sometimes prowess in sports, sometimes school leadership, sometimes another trait or quality, but the test was right in intent. It seems to me of less moment with respect to a particular graduate student whether his grades in book courses are A's and B's than that he should be a healthy human animal with a sense of humor, skill at the piano, the ability to play baseball, a capacity to take long walks, and the training that will enable him to know good food from bad and cheap whisky from civilized drinking. But if you do not like these particular traits and regard them as whimsical, I beg you to set up such of your own as will guarantee in reasonable measure that you are not creating another unhappy bookworm. For, in truth, I know no way to avoid the excess of specialism except to avoid it, and the best way to begin avoiding it is to assure yourself that the human material you are about to deal with is sound, not morbid; humorous and forthright, not withdrawn; somebody, in short, somewhere near capable of fulfilling all the offices both public and private, whether of peace or of war.

QUO VADIS

P. W. Bridgman

It is fashionable to stress the differences between the "sciences" and the "humanities." There are, of course, obvious differences,

From *Daedalus* (The Journal of the American Academy of Arts and Sciences), LXXXVII (Winter, 1958), pp. 85–93. Reprinted by permission.

and for certain purposes and in certain contexts it may be desirable to emphasize them, as, for example, in drawing up a curriculum of instruction or in organizing a university faculty into departments. I believe however, that the differences are more or less superficial, what is common to the sciences and the humanities is far more fundamental and important than the differences. In the first place, both are human enterprises; this gives them a unity which they cannot escape. Furthermore, they are both predominantly intellectual enterprises, even, if I may be permitted to use the term, enterprises of the intelligence. This I would maintain even if we choose to make a concern with values the touchstone of differentiation between the sciences and the humanities. It is often said that science can tell us nothing about values, and that here lies the fundamental distinction between science and the humanities. Perhaps one could by some tour de force set up a definition of science which would forbid it values, but surely one cannot forbid a concern with values to intelligence. Values can be described, analyzed, appraised, and modified, and these are all activities of the intelligence. We cannot act in any situation involving values without engaging in at least some of these activities.

Whether we practice a science or a humanity we cannot avoid exercising our intelligences. It is to some of the consequences of this that I would call your attention. It is, I think, beginning to dawn on us that there is more to this problem of using our minds intelligently than at first strikes the eye. There are techniques of being intelligent. It is not easy to acquire the proper use of the mental tools which we have thoughtlessly inherited or which are implicit in the construction of our brains. Severe effort and long practice are required.

It seems that we are coming to an awareness of the existence and importance of our mental tools from the side of the sciences rather than from the side of the humanities. The reason is not any reflection on the humanities, but is a consequence of human frailty and the fact that the humanities are so much more complex and difficult than the sciences. By far the most important consequence of the conceptual revolution

brought about in physics by relativity and quantum theory lies
not in such details as that meter sticks shorten when they move
or that simultaneous position and momentum have no meaning, but in the insight that we had not been using our minds
properly and that it is important to find out how to do so.
Although it is no reflection on the humanities that this insight
is coming through the comparatively simple situations of physics, I think it *would* be a reflection if this experience of the
sciences did not give the humanities pause, or suggest that it
is almost inevitable that some modification is necessary in their
own conceptual foundations. For would it not be a miracle
if an intellectual apparatus which has evolved to cope with the
primitive situations of daily life and which has been found to
fail when confronted with the comparatively simple needs of
modern physics should retain its validity in the incomparably
more complex situations presented by human society and the
humanities?

SIGNIFICANCE OF DEFINITION: "OPERATIONAL" MEANINGS

Let us now consider in more detail some of the implications
of recent scientific experience for the broader question of what
is involved in the proper use of our minds. One of the most
obvious of the lessons of relativity theory is the importance of
careful attention to the meanings of our words. This attention
to meanings involves much more than heeding the admonition
"define your terms" long accepted by every lawyer and debater.
The objective of the lawyer or debater is primarily to secure
conformity of verbal behavior and thus to permit communication. But conformity and consensus are not enough to ensure
that a term can be used in the way we would like. In fact, the
shocking quality of relativity theory consisted precisely in the
discovery that such a term as "simultaneity," about which there
had been universal agreement when regarded as merely a bit of
verbal behavior, did not have the properties it was assumed to
have outside the universe of verbal behavior. Words have implications in use which are as important as, or more important
than, mere behavioral consensus, and the job of becoming
aware of meanings, includes discovering what these implications
are. Thus many of our terms are, by implication, capable of

being put into statements. A statement, by its very form, implies that it may be true or false. We do not fully know the meaning of a term which is habitually used in statements unless we know whether it makes sense to say that a statement containing the term is either true or false, and still more, unless we can tell what to do to find whether the statement is true or false. This sort of analysis is not often made, and when it is made it often discloses things not suspected.

The physicist has by now found a way of dealing with his meanings which is fairly satisfactory for his purposes, and which does not commit him to preconceptions about fields not yet entered. This method of dealing with meanings I have called "operational." The essence of it is that to know adequately the meaning of a term we must be able to describe what we do when we use it. It is my personal opinion that this way of dealing with meanings has a wider application to all our language, in so far as that language is an activity of intelligence as distinguished from a purely emotional activity; but this is a matter of detail which is more or less beside the point I am trying to make here. This point is that we can always ask what the meaning of any term that we use is, and that in answering this question we have to satisfy *some* criterion of meaning. Whether the criterion is operational or not is not important in this context; there has to be some criterion, and if we can explicitly formulate it, we are in a position to judge from our other experience whether the meaning has the significance we had supposed. It will often be found that the term cannot have the supposed significance, just as the physicist's concept of simultaneity did not. I believe that very few of the terms of humanistic—as distinguished from scientific—import have been subjected to an analysis for meaning as articulate as this, and that when they are thus analyzed the entire situation may appear in a different light. In the case of such humanistic terms as justice, freedom, duty, responsibility or right, it will be found, I believe, that the verbal component is unexpectedly large, and that the meanings are applicable only in a universe which is predominantly verbal. Now it must not be hastily assumed that for this reason we must discard these terms—far from it—but a realization of the situation will, I believe, bring about a change of attitude. The resultant remaking of our concepts is still ahead of us.

Concern with meanings is only one aspect of a growing realization of the extent to which we are verbal animals. Philosophers and logicians are not unaware of this. Consider, for example, the active field of semantics. The realization is growing that the grammar of a language may almost compel certain attitudes. For example, reification is almost inevitable in a language with the structure of English and in other European languages. One cannot say "I do" without implying "I do *something*," and the something becomes reified. The situation is carried over into physics, where the almost universally accepted identity of mass and energy is the result of an unnecessary and illogical reification of energy.

The implications for logic are particularly interesting. It is popularly supposed that logic deals with something fundamental and universal—it was Boole who used the phrase "the laws of thought" in this connection. But one questions the validity of this point of view when one considers that there are languages, such as some of the North American Indian languages, in which it is difficult and uncongenial to formulate a universal statement, and therefore difficult to form a syllogism. Yet the people with such a language manage to meet the situations of daily life with a survival potential about as good as that of the rest of us. It begins to look as though formal logic, as we know it, is an attribute of the group of Indo-European languages with certain grammatical features.

SIGNIFICANCE OF THE OBSERVER IN THOUGHT SYSTEMS

The concern with words is rather near the surface. Physics has had deeper worries and insights, mainly as a result of the development of quantum theory. One of the most important of these insights has been concerned with the role of the observer. Now for the purposes of quantum theory the observer is highly specialized, and is essentially the measuring instrument. A detailed examination of the unavoidable reaction between instrument and object of measurement provides the justification for the Heisenberg Principle of Indetermination. But the point of view of quantum theory has implications for us much wider than the technical details. It forces us to realize that we cannot have information without acquiring that information by some method, and that the story is not complete until we have told both what we know and how we know it. In other words, we have to remember that we always have an observer. Furthermore, this observer is ourselves, and therefore we cannot get away from him. But getting away from itself is what the human race has been trying to do ever since it started philosophizing or worshipping.

Let us face facts and not fear to say out loud that the one field of human activity in which we are most obviously trying to get away from ourselves is the field of religion. This, I take it, is historically true as a statement of what has been involved in the religious activity of the past. The beings and principles which are the concern of religion are beings and principles external to us and independent of us, eternal in the heavens and surrounded with an aura of absolute truth. This absolute truth is thought of as intrinsically knowable, by revelation if not by more mundane methods.

The fact that men have thought in this way has had a most important effect on their overt conduct; one need only consider the Inquisition or the spread of Mohammedanism. In this respect it must be conceded that Toynbee's conception of history is justified, although one may not be willing to assume with Toynbee that the religious attitude must necessarily be as decisive in the future as it has been in the past. Given the view that there exists an absolute truth, and given furthermore the conviction that one has found absolute truth, the intolerance of the Inquisition or the brain-washings of the Communists become logically inevitable. In such a setting, tolerance can be justified only as a Machiavellian measure, to be practiced only while one is too weak to control the social machinery. How secure are we today that the tolerance in which we take so much pride will continue to be accepted as a social virtue? Certainly a large number of our people hold views which if pushed to their logical conclusion would lead straight to intolerance. The reason these people do not act intolerantly is either that they have never thought things through to a logical conclusion or else that they know they do not have the power. I think we have to find other and better reasons for tolerance than any at present widely accepted.

Tolerance is only one of the issues that commonly present themselves in a religious setting. Not only must we find a new basis for tolerance, but we also must re-examine the broader issue of religion as a whole. To do less is to invite the catastrophe which Toynbee foresees for the Western world if our present religious drives are allowed uninhibited play. Since we cannot get away from ourselves, we must find our springs of action within ourselves, a task which the human race has been shirking since the beginning of recorded history. We have to find what admirable motivation is left when we repudiate the almost universal and irrepressible urge of men to get away from themselves, something that we are coming to realize simply cannot be done. It seems to me that we are not going to find how to get along without our absolutes by any "return" to points of view held in the past; rather, something vitally new is required which we can now only faintly glimpse. And there is no reason to fear that our aspirations and ideals will evoke emotions less poignant under the new dispensation than under the old.

SIGNIFICANCE OF GÖDEL'S THEOREM

In this connection the recent experience of mathematicians and logicians with Gödel's theorem is most illuminating. It is a consequence of this theorem that mathematics can never prove that mathematics is free from internal self-contradictions. The realization of this had a tremendous impact, for here was something that the greatest mathematicians had been vainly trying to do. Out of this experience mathematicians and logicians have acquired a new insight—the insight that there are some things that neither they nor anyone else can do with their minds. Perhaps the most devastating point is the realization that the human mind can never have certainty, by either logical, or metaphysical, or mystical methods. The realization that certainty is not logically attainable took Bertrand Russell all his life to acquire, and he acquired it by successively trying in detail one or another purported method of getting certainty —and finding it wanting. Gödel's theorem, as it were, cuts

the Gordian knot with the insight that "certainty" is an illegitimate concept.

The list of illegitimate concepts will certainly grow. For it
is beginning to dawn on us that in the world of mental
activities there may be principles of *impotency* analogous to
the impotency principles of physics. It took a long time to
realize that it is impossible to create energy out of nothing or
that it is impossible to get energy out of a system without
paying the price in terms of entropy. It does not seem un-
reasonable that there should be corresponding principles in the
mental world, or that it should take us longer to discover them,
when we consider the incomparably greater simplicity of the
physical as compared with the mental world. Some day, I have
no doubt, we shall have formulated a set of laws of mental
dynamics analogous to our present laws of thermodynamics.
As it is, we can glimpse at least one such law in the light of
Gödel's theorem. The reason mathematics cannot prove that
mathematics is free from contradiction is that there are some
things a system cannot do with itself. When we try to get away
from ourselves by correcting what our senses or our perceptions or our reason presents us, it is *we* who are attempting to
escape, and whatever the result of the attempt, it will be something of which *we* are aware. Here we have the system dealing
with itself. But what we would like to do can neither be done
nor even be talked about. Perhaps we have here a worthy
candidate for the first law of mental dynamics, namely the law
that we cannot get away from ourselves.

It seems to me that religion is the field of human concern
in which we have most obviously pushed the common-sense
assumption that we can get away from ourselves beyond the
bound of validity, and in so doing are trying to do something
with our minds that cannot be done. It would be rewarding
to look in other directions for examples of intellectual impotency. I suspect that an observer from another planet, con-
templating the inability of our philosophers to reach agreement
on certain questions after three thousand years of effort, would
conclude that in this field we have also been trying to do
something with our minds that cannot be done.

Not only are we beginning to realize the general outlines

of the way the brain can deal with the external world, but we are beginning to get some glimpse of how it works out in detail. Cybernetics, computer technology, and brain physiology, particularly the electrical study of the brain, are all providing valuable insights. Particularly valuable in this connection are the experiments on the nature of perception initiated by Ames and his colleagues at Hanover and now extended to well over a hundred research centers scattered through the world. These experiments are giving an insight into the nature of the perceptions in terms of which we see our world. These perceptions are no simple and immediate reaction to the stimuli acting on the sense organs, but are a most complicated product involving the past history of the brain, and have validity only in a context harmonious with that past experience. The mental machinery having been once conditioned, we have little or no control over the perceptions which ensue. By malicious manipulation it is possible so to arrange the operation of the sense organs that the resulting perceptions are palpably absurd and impossible, but nevertheless have a compulsive quality that can be appreciated only by experiencing it. One cannot see the experiments without asking oneself what is the significance of this compulsion, or, more generally, what is the significance of the compulsion that the entire human race feels in seeing the world as it does? At the very least, it is impossible to retain the conviction that one is seeing something absolute, independent of the seeing mechanism.

THE FUTURE INTELLECTUAL TASK

It will probably be objected that the insights we have been urging are all rather negative and destructive. Something more constructive will doubtless be demanded. But a change of outlook as revolutionary as is contemplated here almost inevitably has to begin by being destructive. Our first concern is whether what we have been saying is true, and destructive criticism may be as true as constructive criticism. If the criticism is true, any reconstruction will at the very least have to meet the objections of the criticism, and, of course, in addition find new constructive factors. I would not admit, however, that we are entirely destitute of constructive insights as to methods of meeting the situation revealed by our criticism. But if I had attempted to argue these constructive possibilities, I would have run the danger of obscuring the main point by introducing elements more controversial even than those I have admitted.

The main point is that the human race has not yet found how to use its mind. We are getting at this realization through the sciences, but the sciences have as yet by no means furnished all the answers. One reason is that for the particular purposes of science an incomplete view is adequate, particularly because the sciences are comparatively so simple. But for the wider purposes of the humanities—the complete human scene in all its scope—some more drastic reconstruction is necessary. It is, for example, obvious that the involvement of the humanities with the whole verbal machinery of thought is much more intimate than that of the sciences. I would place as the most important mark of an adequately educated man a realization that the tools of human thinking are not yet understood, and that they impose limitations of which we are not yet fully aware. As a corollary it follows that the most important intellectual task for the future is to acquire an understanding of the tools, and so to modify our outlook and ideals as to take account of their limitations.

This task is not to be accomplished by any "return" to the insights of the past. The insight that there is any problem here at all is devastatingly new in human history. The sciences and the humanities find themselves facing the problem together; it is too difficult and too pressing to permit the luxury of a division of forces. Appreciation of the existence and the nature of the problem is the first step toward the invention of the new methods and outlooks that will be necessary to solve it.

It seems to me that the human race stands on the brink of a major breakthrough. We have advanced to the point where we can put our hand on the hem of the curtain that separates us from an understanding of the nature of our minds. Is it conceivable that we will withdraw our hand and turn back through discouragement and lack of vision?

QUESTIONS FOR
DISCUSSION AND WRITING

THE TWO CULTURES

1. In what sense are the egotisms of scientists driven by a common purpose? Does Snow prove this point? How important is it to the argument?
2. What is the point of the discussion of Dickens? In view of this comment, is it accurate to speak of two "cultures"? Can you derive a definition of "culture" from Snow's discussion?
3. What is the purpose of contrasting psychoanalysis and cybernetics? Attack or defend Snow's unsupported statement in this contrast.
4. Snow, a novelist and scientist, is one of the outstanding spokesmen for the scientist. What are his main reasons for blaming the humanists more than the scientists? Does this mean he views the humanities as "less valuable" than the sciences?

WHAT SCIENCE IS

1. What kinds of proof does Muller offer in support of his conclusions? In particular, why does he say that "the scientist no more than the poet can afford the illusion that his activity is pure or priestly"? How does he justify including sociology among the sciences? What does this inclusion suggest about scientific data and the scientific method?
2. What does Muller mean when he says that scientists "admire the most wonderful of miracles, that there are not incessant miracles"? How does this statement relate to his discussion of scientific "elegance"? Is "science," as defined by Muller, the same "science" that is criticized by Swift and Dickens?

GULLIVER'S TRAVELS: A VOYAGE TO LAPUTA

1. Swift is attacking both the abstractness of the pure scientist and the absurdity of the technologist. What, in particular, does he ridicule about scientists and technologists? Do you suppose that this is a fair picture of 18th-century science and technology? Is there any way in which it would be applicable to contemporary science and technology?

2. How might a scientist refute Swift's attack? What might he suggest Swift leaves out of the picture?
3. In many ways Swift's prose has exactly the opposite qualities of the things he is describing (and therefore qualifies him as a critic of these things). For example, the description is clear, detailed, vivid, and extremely well organized (see, especially, the description of the construction and use of the pease bladders).
   a. Find other examples of this kind of precision in the passages.
   b. Define carefully the characteristics of the prose which make it so effective.
   c. Write a paragraph, in the manner of Swift, describing the construction and use of some simple object (*e.g.*, a fly swatter, a bathroom plunger).

THE RAMBLER, NUMBER X
1. What point is Johnson trying to make about technology?
2. In your opinion, does the scientist or technologist think of his work in this fashion?
3. Compare Johnson's style in describing a window with a dictionary definition. What is Johnson trying to convey that the dictionary is not? How does the difference between Johnson's intent and the dictionary definition affect the style?

HARD TIMES
1. Dickens suggests that concentration on facts obscures concerns that are more important to mankind. What kind of evidence does he give to support this position? Does this attitude have anything in common with Swift's?
2. Who do you suppose knows more about horses, Bitzer or Sissy Jupe? Although Bitzer's definition is accurate, Dickens obviously disapproves of it. Why? What kind of definition would Dickens prefer? What does this suggest about the nature and function of definition?
3. How do such details as the physical descriptions, the choice of names, and the styles of speech contribute to the point which Dickens seeks to make?

LITERATURE AND SCIENCE
1. In the light of your own education, do you think Arnold was right about whether the "old education" would prevail over the "new"? Do you think he *should* have been right?
2. Does Arnold wish to exclude all study of science from education? Would his definition of "literature" now allow for the inclusion of any works by Einstein or other prominent scientists? How would your history, sociology, algebra, physics, or philosophy texts fit into literature as Arnold understood it?
   Is there any hint of irony in Arnold's discussion of the im-

portance of knowing the function of the "albuminous white of the egg"? What is his argument against making studies of facts such as these (or, in contemporary terms, atomic structure, quantum theory, etc.) central to education? Does it really matter to you personally that the earth travels around the sun? That light is affected by magnetic fields?

3. Arnold here, and Dickens and Swift earlier, have all suggested implicitly or explicitly that science and "facts" are less practical than the study of the humanities. Evaluate this argument. How does Arnold justify it?

4. Arnold's essay here is an answer to Huxley. Would you say he agreed or disagreed with Arnold's view of the proper studies in school? on the meaning of literature? on what is centrally important to ordinary human life?

5. In the light of Fleming's essay, would you say that Arnold's interpretation of Darwin's views of art and religion are accurate?

SCIENCE AND CULTURE

1. This essay provoked Arnold to write his "Literature and Science." Can you discern in Huxley's discussion of "culture" any similarity to the views of Arnold? In advocating scientific education, does Huxley seem to be taking the side of those who, today, disparage liberal education and insist on more practical education, including "adjustment to life"? Would Huxley be likely to prefer modern schools of technology or colleges of arts and sciences?

2. What are the signs in this essay that Huxley, although a renowned scientist, was also learned in literature and the arts? What are the signs that he was an accomplished essayist? Outline the essay to see how Huxley has carefully constructed his arguments to make them most effective. Does the organization reflect a "scientific mind"? Does the quality of the essay confirm Huxley's views on the usefulness of science in education?

3. What is meant by "criticism of life" (read Arnold's essay for further clarification)? How can science help in criticism of life? Would literature or science be most helpful?

4. Both Huxley and Arnold are concerned with what men do once they have achieved relative wealth and comfort in an industrial society. Are there any signs around you today which suggest that their concern was justified? In what sense can modern American prosperity be seen as pointless?

SCIENCE, LITERATURE, AND CULTURE

1. Trilling compares Leavis with Arnold and Snow with Huxley. On what grounds does he do this? Given Trilling's criticism of the personal quality of the Leavis-Snow controversy, what seems to be his reason for the comparison? Which writers does he seem

to admire more, those of the twentieth or those of the nineteenth century? Why?

2. What is the purpose of Trilling's final anecdote about Faraday? How does it relate to the view that the idea of "two cultures" is specious?

3. Trilling attempts to restate Arnold's position, so as to make it more meaningful today, by introducing the concept of "Mind." What is this concept? How successful do you think Mind can be in ordering what Trilling sees as the chaos of contemporary life?

CHARLES DARWIN, THE ANAESTHETIC MAN

1. What apparently was Darwin's main reason for becoming "anaesthetic," that is, for losing his interest in art and culture, and his sensitivity to beauty? Is there evidence that at any time he was unusually sensitive to the beautiful? Do you suppose that all scientists need necessarily reject art and become "fact-and-dust" men like Gradrind in *Hard Times?*

2. In what sense is it possible to see in religion "assent to the evil of the world and acquiescence in it"? Might one see the same thing in Darwin's scientific investigations and science in general? In art?

3. This essay has three main parts. Can you trace the progression of the argument through these parts? Although biographical, the essay is not strictly chronological. Why not? What effects are gained by arranging it differently?

WILLIAM BUTLER YEATS

1. According to Wilson why was it easier for the poet to "express himself both directly and elegantly" in the 16th and 17th centuries? Why, on the other hand, must the modern poet create "a special personality" which "shall shut out or remain indifferent to many aspects of the contemporary world"?

2. Yeats's system is patently absurd to the rational reader and was not completely acceptable even to Yeats himself. Can you suggest why he persisted in using it, why Yeats rejected "Naturalism" (define), and how it is possible to set up a completely imaginary world and yet through it reveal deep familiarity with the problems of the everyday world? How does this problem relate to the view espoused by Swift, Arnold, and Dickens that science is impractical and the humanities practical?

3. Can you see any parallels between the life and attitudes of Yeats and those of Darwin? Is Darwin's rejection of the "unreal" the result of a discontent with life similar to that of Yeats, who seems to have rejected the "real" in his poetry?

4. According to Wilson's description, whose response to the problems of contemporary life seems more meaningful, Yeats's or

Shaw's? What are these problems? Are Yeats and Shaw actually responding to the same problems? Are Yeats and Darwin?

THOSE SKILLED BARBARIANS

1. What is Furlong's purpose in writing this article? Is it an attack, an attempt to analyze causes, an attempt to suggest ways of overcoming a genuine difficulty?
2. What famous men went to your school? Did their undergraduate studies prepare them for their eventual careers? Should they have?
3. What is so absurd about the responses of the students to Ogden Nash's poem? What does the poem really mean?

REASON

1. This story is, in part, about the dangers of approaching life from a strictly logical and scientific point of view. How real is this danger? What are the consequences? Is the danger greater now than at the time of Dickens and Swift?
2. Given the developments in cybernetics over the past few years, developing a robot like Cutie becomes increasingly probable. Given his intellectual powers, his infallibility (barring mechanical breakdown), and his strength and agility, does not such a robot seem preferable to man himself? Ought he not be in a position to dominate man?
3. In contrast to Dickens and Swift, Asimov does not obviously take sides. If you were a robot reading this story, would you side with Cutie or Donovan and Powell? Why? What does this suggest about the nature of Asimov's style?

WHO AM I AND WHO ARE YOU?

1. Discuss the method Steinberg uses in bringing his students to an awareness of the limitation of science. In particular discuss the effectiveness of his analogies. Would you agree with the conclusions to which Steinberg led his class—that science provides "no entrance" into the world of self-definition?
2. The language of Steinberg's essay is deliberately colloquial. Give examples of particularly colloquial phrasing. Considering Steinberg's purpose, what use does this colloquialism serve? What attitude toward his subject and his students does his language reveal?

SCIENTIST AND HUMANIST: CAN THE MINDS MEET?

1. Rabi's position is very similar to Snow's. In what ways is it different? Given the fact that Snow's piece appeared at about the same time as Rabi's, can you suggest by reference both to content and style why Snow's piece made a greater impact? Whose arguments do you feel are better?

2. Compare Rabi's "wisdom" with Arnold's "the best that has been thought and said." Given the similarity in their ultimate goals, what do you think accounts for the difference in their attitudes toward science? Do they share a commitment to the interdisciplinary approach?
3. Are students "the only broadly educated body in the university community"? Do you ever feel while listening to lectures that the lecture would be more valuable if the teacher were widely educated outside of his specialty?
4. Faculty members, while undergraduates, were probably "broadly educated" also. Does this fact reflect the inadequacy of "broad education" or the demands society makes on its professional classes? Would the methods Steinberg proposes alleviate these difficulties?

THE TREE OF KNOWLEDGE
1. In what ways does the fact that Oppenheimer is addressing a group of reporters influence the way in which he writes the essay? Does Oppenheimer seem to be "talking down"? What devices does Oppenheimer use to make intelligible the "unintelligibility" of technical science?
2. Oppenheimer and Rabi agree that there is a communications barrier between science and the humanities. Does what Oppenheimer says about this barrier suggest that Rabi's solution is ultimately ineffectual?
3. In one sense Oppenheimer is trying to do for science the same things Jones is doing for the humanities. Compare the tone and strategies of the two articles (why, e.g., is Jones consistently ironic and comic, Oppenheimer serious and direct? Why does Jones urge alterations in the methods of studying and talking about the humanities while Oppenheimer, for the most part, merely warns the public about the difficulties in understanding science?).
4. What are Oppenheimer's grounds for believing in a harmoniously ordered natural world? Does this view of the universe conflict with Darwin's? Which position offers greatest hope for a reunification of science and the humanities?

THE HUMANITIES AND THE COMMON READER
1. Is it possible that humanistic studies are just as difficult technically as Oppenheimer says scientific studies are? In the light of Jones's discussion of jargon, what do you think Jones's answer would be?
2. Jones makes certain assumptions about the kinds of humanistic interests a common reader is likely to have. What are these assumptions? Define the common reader carefully for yourself, and suggest how adequately Jones describes what will interest

him. Is Jones's essay written for the "common reader"? What evidence in language, allusions, and structure do you have?

3. According to what standards does Jones condemn contemporary humanistic study? Does he seriously invoke science as an example to the humanists?

QUO VADIS

1. This essay is highly abstract, making casual reference to scientific discoveries and ideas which are not likely to be well known to the layman. You ought, of course, to look up words that seem strange (*e.g.*, what does "reified" mean?). But how important is it that you understand fully the quantum theory, or Gödel's theorem, in order to understand the essay? For what kind of audience does the essay seem to be written? Can you justify its abstractness? Can you supply examples that Bridgman doesn't take time for in order to clarify his meaning: for example, can you give an example or examples to support the idea that "we can't get away from ourselves"?

2. In the light of the views of such writers as Swift, Dickens, Arnold, and Asimov, what do you think of Bridgman's idea that we shall some day "formulate a set of laws of mental dynamics analogous to our present laws of thermodynamics"? (Is it, by the way, necessary to know the laws of thermodynamics to answer this question intelligently?)

3. In what sense is it possible to say that religion is the field in which "we are most obviously trying to get away from ourselves"? Why should people feel the urge to get away from themselves? Does the application of Gödel's theorem, that there are things which the human mind simply can't handle, make this urge more comprehensible? What relation has this to the idea that "we can't get away from ourselves"?

4. Bridgman says that the subject matter of the humanities is more complex and difficult than that of the sciences. Does this seem to be borne out by your own experiences in class? If you agree with this position, have any of the essays in this book strengthened this view for you? Are there any essays included here which seem to contradict this view?

SELECTED BIBLIOGRAPHY

Aristophanes, *Clouds*
A. J. Ayer, *Language, Truth, and Logic*
Francis Bacon, *The New Atlantis*
Bertolt Brecht, *Galileo*
Albert Camus, *The Myth of Sisyphus*
K. G. Collier, "The Impact of Science on the Western View of Life," in *Hibbert Journal* (January, 1949)
A. H. Compton, *The Human Meaning of Science*
James B. Conant, *Modern Science and Modern Man*
R. F. Davidson, *The Humanities in Contemporary Life*
Herbert Dingle, *Through Science to Philosophy*
René Dubos, *Dreams of Reason*
William H. George, *The Scientist in Action*
S. G. Hacker, "Possible Humanistic Aspects of Science," in *Popular Astronomy* (May, 1951)
Julian Harris, *The Humanities*
Aldous Huxley, *Brave New World*
T. H. Huxley, *Culture and Education*
Karl Jaspers, "Is Science Evil?" in *Commentary* (March, 1950)
B. C. Kenney, "Dead Horse Flogged Again," in *Speculum* (October, 1955)
H. Kenniston, "Humanities in a Scientific World," in *Annals of the American Academy*
F. R. Leavis, *Two Cultures? The Significance of C. P. Snow*
Lucretius, *On the Nature of Things*
R. A. Millikan, *Science and Life*
H. J. Muller, *Science and Criticism*
H. Myers, "Literature, Science, and Democracy," in *Pacific Spectator* (1954)
John Henry Newman, *Scope and Nature of a University Education*
George Orwell, *1984*
Max Otto, *Science and the Moral Life*
T. M. Pearce, "Humanities in the Modern World," in *Pacific Spectator* (1953)
A. D. C. Peterson, "How to Break the Barrier Between Science and the Arts," in *The New Scientist* (November 22, 1956)
Plato, "Ion"
Rabelais, *Gargantua; Pantagruel*
D. D. Raphael, "Art and the Sciences," in *Confluence* (Spring, 1957)
I. A. Richards, *Science and Poetry*
L. N. Ridenour, "Science, the Humanities, and Education," in *Virginia Quarterly Review* (1954)
J. J. Rousseau, *Émile*
Bertrand Russell, *Mysticism and Logic*
Science Advisory Committee, *Education for the Age of Science*
C. P. Snow, "Conflict of Cultures," in *Saturday Evening Post* (September 12, 1959)
———, *The Masters*
———, *The New Men*
———, *Two Cultures and the Scientific Revolution*
T. L. Stoddard, *Scientific Humanism*
J. W. N. Sullivan, *Limitations of Science*
A. N. Whitehead, *Science and the Modern World*
C. M. Woodhouse, "Science and Humanism: An Unreal Debate?" in *Nineteenth Century* (May, 1950)